Interactions I
Workbook

Interactions I

A Cognitive Approach to
Beginning Chinese

Workbook

Margaret Mian Yan **Jennifer Li-chia Liu**
嚴棉   劉力嘉

Indiana University Press
Bloomington and Indianapolis

This book is a publication of

INDIANA UNIVERSITY PRESS
601 North Morton Street
Bloomington, IN 47404-3797 USA

http://www.indiana.edu/~iupress

Telephone orders 800-842-6796
Fax orders 812-855-7931
Orders by email iuporder@indiana.edu

Cataloging information is available from the Library of Congress.

By Margaret Mian Yan and Jennifer Li-chia Liu
ISBN 978-0-253-21122-4 paperback (Interactions I)
ISBN 978-0-253-21202-3 paperback (Interactions I: Workbook)

By Jennifer Li-chia Liu and Margaret Mian Yan
ISBN 978-0-253-21123-1 paperback (Interactions II)
ISBN 978-0-253-21203-0 paperback (Interactions II: Workbook)
ISBN 978-0-253-21201-6 paperback (Interactions I & II: Teacher's Manual)

5   6   7   8   12   11   10

Contents

Preface

This ***Workbook*** is designed to complement the student text ***Interactions I: A Cognitive Approach to Beginning Chinese*** and to give students of diverse background a variety of practice with spoken as well as written Chinese.

All the exercises are written based on the communicative approach to language teaching and arranged to facilitate the acquisition of discrete language points and practice in all four language skills. In addition, the awareness of cultural differences is encouraged. Thus whenever possible, we have contextualized the exercises by providing a realistic and meaningful situation for the use of Chinese in the hopes of establishing a link between language study and reality.

For the first three lessons, exercises are created to check students' preconception of Chinese language and their knowledge of the sound system and the writing principles. From Lesson 4 through Lesson 13, we include both language-focused discrete practice and skill-oriented synthesized task. The exercises, divided into seven sections, follow the sequence: Vocabulary, Character, Grammar, Listening, Speaking, Reading, and Writing.

It is recommended that the workbook exercises be assigned *selectively* after each lesson in the student text is presented. An array of exercises is created to meet students' various needs and to lessen teachers' preparation time. For example, a speaking proficient student like many ethnic Chinese should be asked to work more on reading and writing than on speaking and listening. The Speaking and Grammar section can be done in class. The Listening section can be saved for quizzes. The section on characters and writing can be used as homework. In sum, students are *not* expected to complete all the exercises in each lesson.

The Listening sections are designed to be used with the accompanying audiotapes. The tapescripts for the Listening section recorded on cassettes as well as the answer key for some exercises are given in the teacher's manual. Some visuals in the book are created in Corel Draw and some adapted from the clip arts in Corel Gallery by Corel Corporation, 1994. Most of the authentic reading materials included in the Reading section are from the World Journal 世界日報 Shìjiè Rìbào published in New York (1997) and first/second grade reader 國語課本 Guóyǔ Kèběn compiled by National Institute for Compilation and Translation 國立編譯館 Guólì Biānyìguǎn in Taiwan (1996/1997). We would like to express our sincere gratitude to these two institutions for their permission to include their materials in our workbook. We would like also to thank the following business firms/companies for allowing us to use their advertisements in the workbook and helping students to enhance their Chinese reading competence: 永聰軒 Chung's Cantonese & Mandarin [Cuisine], 世界書局 W. J. Bookstore, 中國書店 Central China Book Company, 東方職業介紹所 Atlantic

Employment Agency, 大通電訊 Primus Telecommunications Inc., 上海四五六菜館 Moon Palace Restaurant, and 健安堂藥材公司 Ken On Tong Herbs, Inc., 華美中醫 康復中心 Hoami [Traditional Chinese Medicine Recovery Center], 李富華汽車維修 中心 Vinnes Auto Service Center, and 藍天旅遊 Wings Travel and Tours. Last but not least, we would like to thank Kenneth Goodall, Paul Manfredi, and Lara Ingeman for their editorial help.

                                                                      The Authors

第 一 課 緒 論

A. Before you read Lesson 1, list five things you know and don't know about Chinese language and culture. Discuss them with your teachers and classmates.

I know…   I don't know…

1. _____   1. _____

2. _____   2. _____

3. _____   3. _____

4. _____   4. _____

5. _____   5. _____

B. Study Lesson 1 and answer the following questions.

_____ 1. Which language family does Chinese belong to?
        a. Austronesian family   c. Altaic family
        b. Sino-Tibetan family   d. Austro-Asiatic family

_____ 2. Which dialect is the Chinese National Language?
        a. Wu   c. Yue
        b. Min   d. Mandarin

_____ 3. Which is true?
        a. Chinese has a distinction between singular and plural nouns.
        b. Chinese doesn't have a distinction between singular and plural nouns.

_____ 4. Which is true?
        a. Chinese uses stress to distinguish different morphemes.
        b. Chinese uses pitch to distinguish different morphemes.

_____ 5. What is Chinese basic word order?
        a. SVO   c. OSV
        b. SOV   d. VSO

_____ 6. Which is true?
        a. In Chinese, the modifier always precedes the modified.
        b. In Chinese, the modified always precedes the modifier.

第 二 課　發 音 入 門

A. Recognizing Tones
Listen to the tapes and choose the syllable with the correct tone.

_____   1.   a. ā   b. ǎ   c. à
_____   2.   a. ǐ   b. í   c. ī
_____   3.   a. wǔ   b. wù   c. wú
_____   4.   a. fēi   b. féi   c. fěi
_____   5.   a. dōu   b. dòu   c. dǒu

B. Recognizing Initials
Listen to the tapes and choose the correct syllable.

_____   1.   a. bē   b. pē   c. dē
_____   2.   a. dá   b. tá   c. pá
_____   3.   a. gè   b. kè   c. tè
_____   4.   a. zǐ   b. jǐ   c. zhǐ
_____   5.   a. zhī   b. chī   c. zī
_____   6.   a. sū   b. shū   c. zū
_____   7.   a. zhù   b. jù   c. shù
_____   8.   a. shú   b. zhǔ   c. zú

C. Recognizing Finals
Listen to the tapes and choose the correct syllable.

_____   1.   a. xiē   b. xuē   c. shuī
_____   2.   a. qiǔ   b. xiǔ   c. jiǔ
_____   3.   a. cuì   b. zhuì   c. chuì
_____   4.   a. yāng   b. yān   c. yuān
_____   5.   a. kè   b. gè   c. guò

D. Recognizing tones in combinations

Listen to the tapes and choose the correct combinations.

_____	1.	a. xīngqì	b. xíngqí	c. xīngqī
_____	2.	a. hēchà	b. hēchá	c. hèchà
_____	3.	a. gōngkē	b. gǒngkè	c. gōngkè
_____	4.	a. míng.tiān	b. mìng.tián	c. mǐngtiān
_____	5.	a. lāoshī	b. lāoshǐ	c. lǎoshī

E. Practicing pronunciation

1. Read the following syllables in rows from left to right.

	1st Tone	2nd Tone	3rd Tone	4th Tone
a.	ā	á	ǎ	à
b.	āi	ái	ǎi	ài
c.	ēi	éi	ěi	èi
d.	iū	iú	iǔ	iù
e.	āo	áo	ǎo	ào
f.	uō	uó	uǒ	uò
g.	uī	uí	uǐ	uì

2. Read the following syllables in rows from left to right.

a.	bā	pā	dú	tú
b.	guài	kuài	zǎo	cǎo
c.	zhī	chī	zhū	chū
d.	shì	shù	rén	róu
e.	jǐ	qǐ	jù	qù
f.	xí	xú	yuè	què
g.	jué	xué	dōu	duō
h.	xiě	xuě	gè	kè

3. Read the following syllables in rows from left to right.

a.	chūqù	sùshè	chìzǐ	chǐcùn	cíjù	cíxù
b.	cìxù	cìjī	cízhí	cùyì	jíshì	jícù
c.	suànshù	suāncù	zīzhù	zīxùn	zìzhù	zìrán
d.	zìzhǐ	zìzhù	zìxué	zìjué	jísù	jíxū
e.	jìsù	shùzì	shùzhī	shísù	chísù	sìshí
f.	shísì	zìsī	xísú	zhǔyì	zhùyì	zhǔchí

第三課　漢字簡介

A. Recognizing stroke types

1. Circle the stroke type identified in the first column in the following characters.

a.	Horizontal stroke	呈	青　非
b.	Vertical stroke	史	中　正
c.	Left stroke	八	火　刀
d.	Right stroke	為	衣　近
e.	Dot	心	汁　馬
f.	Hook	西	丁　狗
g.	Turning stroke	曰	又　九
h.	Rising stroke	以	折　求

2. How many strokes do the following characters have?

_____ a. 子　　　_____ f. 店
_____ b. 王　　　_____ g. 魚
_____ c. 公　　　_____ h. 國
_____ d. 出　　　_____ i. 學
_____ e. 西　　　_____ j. 鳥

B. Recognizing and practicing stroke orders

1. Circle the character(s) which begin with the same stroke as the ones already circled.

a.　不　(生)　元　我　明
b.　行　學　這　(記)　們
c.　並　門　必　用　(是)
d.　(去)　老　半　女　把
e.　的　那　(師)　花　來

2. Write the characters using the correct stroke order (one character per box)　　**Worksheet 1**

Hàn zì	一	二	三	四	五	六	七	八	九	十
Notes	yī one 1 stroke	èr two 2	sān three 3	sì four 5	wǔ five 4	liù six 4	qī seven 2	bā eight 2	jiǔ nine 2	shí ten 2
1										
2										
3										
4										
5										
6										

	Compound/Phrase/Sentence/Memory Aid
一	My phone number:
二	My friend's phone number:
三	My teacher's phone number:
四	My teacher's office number:
五	My address or room number:
六	My license number:
七	This year:
八	The year I was born:
九	The year I plan to graduate from this university:
十	The number of people in my family:

C. Getting familiar with the formation of characters
   Draw a line to connect the characters with their meaning.

1. Pictographs		2. Indicatives		3. Ideatives (ideological compounds)	
木	rain	下	root	林 (木+木)(tree+tree)	to open
水	mountain	凸	branch	男 (田+力)(farm+power)	peace
雨	moon	本	down	信 (亻+言)(human+words)	woods
山	tree	末	concave	安 (宀+女)(house+woman)	male
月	water	凹	convex	開 (門+手)(door+hand)	truth

4. Harmonics (phonetic compounds)	
情 qíng(忄+青)(heart+qīng)	eye
清 qīng(氵+青)(water+qīng)	sunny
請 qǐng(言+青)(speech+qīng)	feelings
晴 qíng(日+青)(sun+qīng)	clear
睛 jīng(目+青)(eye+qīng)	please

D. Recognizing different writing styles
   Try to match the characters with their various writing styles.

1.	床	光	明	6.	疑	地	霜
2.	前	月	床	7.	是	霜	上
3.	明	床	月	8.	地	是	疑
4.	月	前	光	9.	上	疑	是
5.	光	明	前	10.	霜	上	地

E. Simplifying traditional Chinese characters
   Check with your teachers or Chinese friends and find out the simplified form for the following characters.

	Full Form	Simplified Form		Full Form	Simplified Form
1.	門	门	7.	號	
2.	車		8.	國	
3.	個		9.	學	
4.	這		10.	書	
5.	課		11.	難	
6.	誰		12.	愛	

F. Recognizing radicals

1. Circle the radical of each character and find out the meaning for each radical.

		Meaning of the radical			Meaning of the radical
a.	他		n.	明	
b.	姓		o.	草	
c.	唱		p.	疼	
d.	紅		q.	眼	
e.	很		r.	松	
f.	拍		s.	錢	
g.	刻		t.	志	
h.	話		u.	洋	
i.	堆		v.	煙	
j.	努		w.	筆	
k.	晴		x.	電	
l.	開		y.	館	
m.	鮭		z.	輪	

2. Draw a line to link the characters that share the same radical with the characters in column two:

課	叫	話
賭	林	貴
河	說	塊
姓	打	洗
喝	們	媽
休	買	唱
柏	地	拉
推	江	你
培	好	材

G. Looking up a character in a dictionary

Use any Chinese dictionary to find out the meaning of the following characters.

1. 京　jīng _____
2. 公　gōng _____
3. 困　kùn _____
4. 爸　bà _____
5. 朋　péng _____
6 晶　jīng _____
7 氧　yǎng _____
8 狼　láng _____
9 珠　zhū _____
10. 筍　sǔn _____

第四課 今天是幾月幾號？

I. Vocabulary

A. Look at the following pictures and fill in the appropriate new words in pinyin.

1.

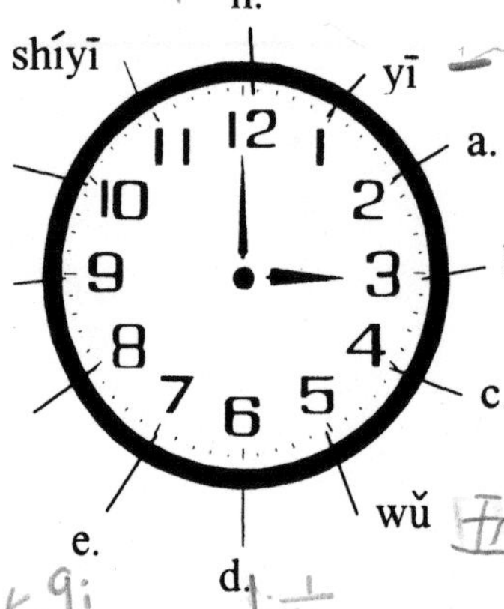

[handwritten annotations on clock image:]

十二 h.
十一 shíyī
十 shí g.
九 jiǔ
八 bā
七 qī e.
六 d.
五 wǔ c. sì 四
b. 三 sān
a. 二 er
yī 一

diǎn 点 o'clock 1:30
一点三十分 fēng minute
1:050
一点 零五分 kīng
ask time 几点？

2.

a.   b.

June 1996						
星期日	星期一	星期二	星期三	星期四	星期五	星期六
						1
2	3	4	5	6	7	8
9	10	11	12	13	14	15
16	17	18	19	20	21	22
23/30	24	25 a.	26	27	28	29

c.   d.   jīn.tiān   e.   f.

3.

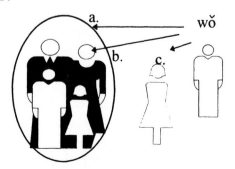

a.   wǒ
b.
c.

The word here will probably
be: d.

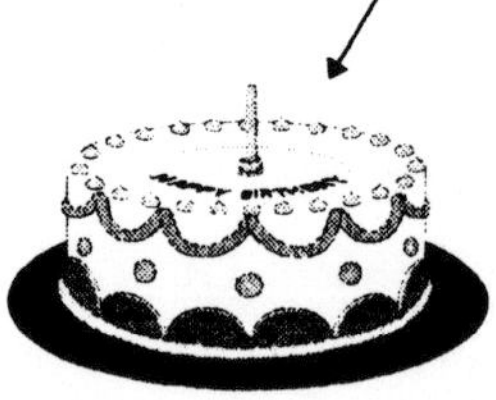

II. Characters

Hàn zì	你	我	是	不	大	小	學	生	上	下
Notes	nǐ you 7	wǒ I, me 7	shì to be 9	bù no, not 4	dà big 3	xiǎo small 3	xué to study 15	shēng to be born 5	shàng up 3	xià down 3
1										
2										
3										
4										
5										
6										

	Compound/Phrase/Sentence/Memory Aid
你	
我	
是	
不	
大	
小	
學	
生	
上	
下	

Worksheet 3

Hàn zì	課	嗎	的	日	月	幾	明	天	他	哪
Notes	kè class 15	.ma particle 13	.de particle 8	rì sun 4	yuè moon 4	jǐ how many 12	míng bright 8	tiān day, sky 4	tā he, him 5	nǎ which 10
1										
2										
3										
4										
5										
6										

	Compound/Phrase/Sentence/Memory Aid
課	
嗎	
的	
日	
月	
幾	
明	
天	
他	
哪	

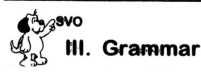

SVO

III. Grammar

⬤ Major Sentence Patterns

1. From Whole to Part Principle

> Whole 〉 Part
> (largest unit 〉 smallest unit)

1. You want to send a letter to your Chinese pen pal, 李美 in Beijing, China. (Běijīng, Zhōngguó) She lives in the room 245, Girls' Dorm #8 (Èrsìwǔ hào fáng, Nǚshēng dìbā sùshè). Please fill out the following envelope.

2. Say the following time expressions. Then take turns saying each day and date to a classmate while s/he writes them.

   a. Wednesday, June 20, 1964
   b. Monday, November 25, 1934
   c. Friday, July 31, 1982
   d. Sunday, May 21, 1995
   e. Tuesday, February 5, 1972
   f. Saturday, September 3, 1957

2. Equational sentences

S + Equative Verb + O			S 是 O	S 也是 O
(N/NP)	(EV)	(N/NP)	S 不是 O	S 也不是 O

Answer the following questions using the pattern provided in the above chart.

1. 今天是幾月幾號？

   _____

2. 明天是星期六嗎？

   _____

3. 你是大學生(college student)嗎？ 李明呢？

_____

4. 高德中是美國人 (American) 嗎？ 你呢？

_____

3. Choice-type (A-not-A) questions

S　是不是　O？	是/對了, S　是　O 不/不是, S　不是　O

Generate questions for the following dialogues using the pattern provided in the chart.

1. _____ ?

是，她是中國人。

2. _____ ?

不，他的生日不是五月五號。

3. _____ ?

不，昨天是九月十二號。

4. 嗎 questions

S　是　O　嗎？	是/對了，S　是　O 不/不是，S　不是　O

1. _____ ?

對了，Christmas 是十二月二十五號。

2. _____ ?

不，她不是美國中學生 (middle school student)。

3. _____ ?

不是，他是中國大學生。

5. Question-word questions

S 是 星期幾？	S 是 星期 no.
S 是 幾月幾號？	S 是 no. 月 no. 號
S 哪一天 V O？	S Time When V O
S 是 誰？	S 是 X
# 月 # 號是誰的生日？	no. 月 no. 號是 X 的生日

1. July 4th 是星期幾？

_____

2. Halloween 是幾月幾號？

_____

3. 你哪一天開學？

_____

4. 他是誰？

_____

5. 二月二十二號是誰的生日？

_____

6. Stative verbs/adjectives

S + (adv) + SV
Adj + N

1. 她很小。　　　→　☐ SV　　☐ Adj

2. 小學生　　　　→　☐ SV　　☐ Adj

3. 他很不快樂。　→　☐ SV　　☐ Adj

B Usage of Common Phrases

1. The question particle 呢

S₁ 是 X，S₂ 呢？	S₁ is X, how about S₂?
S₁ Time When V O，S₂ 呢？	S₁ Time When V O, how about S₂?

1. You overheard a conversation between Xiao Li and Xiao Gao. Fill in the blanks of the dialogue with the cues given in the chart.

	Registration	Class Start	Birthday	Nationality
小高	後天(8/27)	下星期一(8/30)	8/23	美國人
小李	明天(8/26)	下星期二(8/31)	8/26	中國人

Gao:　我的生日是＿＿＿＿＿＿＿＿＿，＿＿＿＿＿＿？

Li:　我的生日也是八月。我明天註册，＿＿＿＿＿？

Gao:　我＿＿＿＿＿註册，＿＿＿＿＿上課。＿＿＿＿＿？

Li:　我＿＿＿＿＿上課。

 IV. Listening

1. Which is true about Xiao Li's birthday?
   a. It's on September 3.
   b. It's on September 10.
   c. It's on September 4.
   d. It's on September 12.

2. Which statement is true about the dialogue?
   a. Both speakers registered yesterday.
   b. Both speakers will go to classes next Monday.
   c. A's school starts tomorrow and B's school started already.
   d. A will go to classes on Monday but B on Tuesday.

3. Listen to the statements and help Xiao Li mark his calendar for important dates and events that he should remember.

	星期日	星期一	星期二	星期三	星期四	星期五	星期六
八月	18	19	20 生日	21	22	23	24
	25	26	27	28	29	30	31
九月	1	2	3	4	5	6	7
	8	9	10	11	12	13	14

V. Speaking

A. Talk about yourself
Use the following questions as cues.

1. 你幾月幾號註冊？星期幾開學？

2. 你哪一天上課？

3. 我是大學生，你呢？

4. 你幾月幾號生日？

B. Cheerleading with numbers
The following chant is commonly used by Chinese students and audiences to cheer for their favorite team. Try it to practice your numbers.

Yī èr sān, sān èr yī
Yī èr sān sì wǔ liù qī
Qī liù wǔ sì sān èr yī
Zhōng.guó xué.shēng dé dìyī
                    (to get first place)

一二三，三二一
一二三四五六七
七六五四三二一
[中國學生] 得第一
(substitute this with name of a team
or a person)

C. Find a partner and use a three month calendar to practice asking and saying the days of the week and each month in Chinese. Use affirmative and negative sentence structure, and question word/choice type questions.

VI. Reading

A. Read the Text
Check your comprehension of the lesson dialogue by deciding whether the statements are true or false.

T / F   1. Lǐ Míng míng.tiān zhùcè, Gāo Dézhōng jīn.tiān zhùcè.

李明明天註冊，高德中今天註冊。

T / F   2. Gāo Dézhōng bāyuè sānshíyīhào shàngkè.

高德中八月三十一號上課。

T / F   3. Gāo Dézhōng .de shēng.rì shì bāyuè èrshísānhào.

高德中的生日是八月二十三號。

T / F　4.　Lǐ Míng .de shēng.rì yě shì bāyuè
　　　　 èrshísānhào.

李明的生日也是八月二十三
號。

T / F　5.　"Jīn.tiān" shì bāyuè èrshíwǔhào.

「今天」是八月二十五號。

B. Read the Journal

Read the following journal and indicate whether the statements below are true or false.

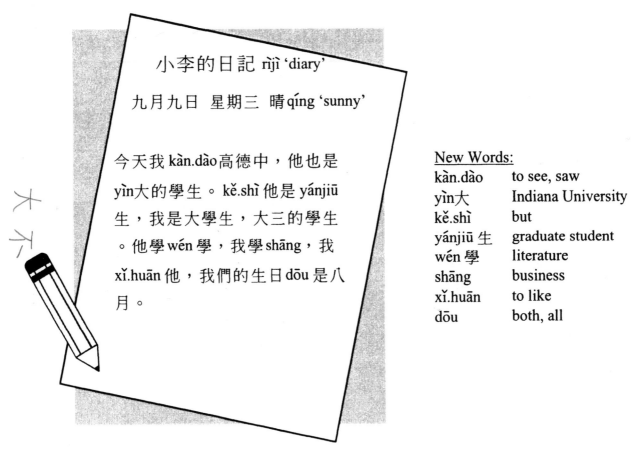

小李的日記 rìjì 'diary'

九月九日　星期三　晴 qíng 'sunny'

今天我 kàn.dào高德中，他也是
yìn大的學生。kě.shì 他是 yánjiū
生，我是大學生，大三的學生
。他學 wén 學，我學 shāng，我
xǐ.huān 他，我們的生日 dōu 是八
月。

New Words:

kàn.dào	to see, saw
yìn大	Indiana University
kě.shì	but
yánjiū 生	graduate student
wén 學	literature
shāng	business
xǐ.huān	to like
dōu	both, all

T / F　1. Both Xiao Li and Xiao Gao are students at Indiana University.

T / F　2. Xiao Li is a senior this year and Xiao Gao is a graduate student.

T / F　3. Xiao Li and Xiao Gao have different majors.

T / F　4. Xiao Li does not like Xiao Gao because he is a graduate student.

T / F　5. Xiao Li and Xiao Gao have different birthdays.

C. Read the Authentic Material

1. Read the following clipping from the Chinese newspaper 世界日報 shìjiè rìbào '[world-border-day-newspaper] World Journal' and fill in the following blanks.

This newspaper was issued (in New York) on:

Month and day: ＿＿＿＿＿＿＿＿＿＿＿＿＿＿

Day of the week: ＿＿＿＿＿＿＿＿＿＿＿＿＿＿

Note: In general, paragraphs in Chinese newspapers consist of paragraphs of either vertical or horizontal lines of characters. Paragraphs of vertical lines of characters are read from top to bottom and from right to left. In contrast, paragraphs of horizontal lines are read from top to bottom and from left to right as in English. Headlines in some newspapers (e.g., World Journal, Central Daily News, etc.) are read from right to left, and others are read from left to right (e.g., Renmin Ribao, etc.).

2. Circle or highlight the characters in this newspaper clipping that you have learned so far.

3. Read the following clipping from the Chinese newspaper 人民日報 Rénmín
   Rìbào '[people-day-newspaper] People's Daily' and fill in the following blanks.

   This newspaper was issued (in Beijing) on:

   Month and day: _____

   Day of the week: _____

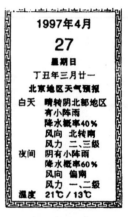

4. Read the following clipping from the Chinese newspaper 中央日報 Zhōngyāng Rìbào
   '[central-day-newspaper] Central Daily News' and fill in the following blanks.

   This newspaper was issued (in Taiwan) on:

   Month and day: _____

   Day of the week: _____

VII. Writing

A. Write the pinyin and the tone marks for the following sentences.

1. 我前天註冊，明天開學，八月二十六號、星期一上課。

2. 下星期天不是九月四號嗎？

3. 祝你生日快樂！

B. Complete the following paragraph by filling in the appropriate words with their corresponding number.

Hints　1. 也　2. 對　3. 呢　4. 幾　5. 哪　6. 嗎　7. 們　8. 的　9. 不　10. 是　11. 下

我是大學生，我 _8_ 朋友 _1_ 是大學生。我 _10_ 昨天註冊， _7_ 是今天註冊

，你 _3_ ？你星期 _5_ 註冊？ ___ 一天開學？你 ___ 星期一上課 ___ ？

C. Follow the format below and write a birthday card to your friend or relative.

Happy Birthday　Happy Birthday　Happy Birthday

　　小李：

　　　　　　　祝　你

　　　　生 日 快 樂 !

德中
　　賀

八月二十六日

賀 hè 'to
congratulate'

第五課 你今天有沒有課？

I. Vocabulary

A. Check the "time words" in the following list and write their meaning in English.

☐ 1. Rìwén   日文   _____   ☐ 5. dǎgōng   打工   _____

☐ 2. zhōumò   週末   _____   ☐ 6. měitiān   每天   _____

☐ 3. xià.wǔ   下午   _____   ☐ 7. xiū.xí   休息   _____

☐ 4. shén.me   什麼   _____   ☐ 8. yù.bèi   預備   _____

B. Choose the right word to complete the following sentences.

1. Tā měitiān (děi, dōu, gēn) yǒu kè.   他每天(得、都、跟)有課。

2. Xiǎo Gāo míng.tiān zuò (jǐ, něi yì tiān,   小高明天做(幾、哪一天、什麼)？
    shén.me)?

3. Wǒ tiān.tiān děi shàng (Zhōngwénkè,   我天天得上(中文課、中午、功課)。
    zhōngwǔ, gōngkè).

C. Fill out the following schedule (功課表 gōngkèbiǎo) for yourself, indicating when you go to what classes and when you would take a break (休息 xiū.xí), work (打工 dǎgōng) or do your homework (做功課 zuò gōngkè).

姓名	功課表						_____年
	星期一	星期二	星期三	星期四	星期五	星期六	星期日
上午							
中午							
下午							

II. Characters　　　　　　　　　　　　　**Worksheet 4**

Hàn zì	今	年	有	沒	中	午	國	文	兩	個
Notes	jīn today 4	nián year 6	yǒu to have 6	méi have not 7	zhōng middle 4	wǔ noon 4	guó nation 11	wén language 4	liǎng two 8	.ge M 10
1										
2										
3										
4										
5										
6										

Compound/Phrase/Sentence/Memory Aid

今
年
有
沒
中
午
國
文
兩
個

Hàn zì	朋	友	早	做	什	麼	跟	也	都	呢
Notes	péng friend 8	yǒu friend 4	zǎo early 6	zuò to do 11	shén what 4	.me suffix 14	gēn with 13	yě also, too 3	dōu all 11	.ne particle 8
1										
2										
3										
4										
5										
6										

	Compound/Phrase/Sentence/Memory Aid
朋	
友	
早	
做	
什	
麼	
跟	
也	
都	
呢	

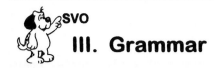

III. Grammar

① Major Sentence Patterns

1. Noun phrases

> Noun Phrase → Noun + Noun
> NP → Day + Forenoon/afternoon/evening
> NP → No. + Measure Word (M) + N

1. Write the meaning of the following noun phrases in English.

中文 ＋ 老師 → *Chinese teacher*
日文 ＋ 學生 → *Japanese student*
英文 ＋ 課　→ *English class*

2. Match columns two and three to generate the following phrases.

Yesterday afternoon　昨天　晚上
This morning　今天　下午
Tomorrow evening　明天　上午

3. 一＿＿年有五十二＿＿＿星期，一＿＿星期有七＿＿天，一＿＿天有二十四＿＿
小時(xiǎoshí 'hours')。

2. The possessive verb 有 — 嗎 form

S MTA (也)(都) 有 O .ma？	對(了), S MTA (也)(都) 有　　O 不,　　S MTA (也)(都) 沒(有) O
S (MTA) (Neg) V O, 也 (Neg) V O S (MTA) (不) 是 A,　也 (不) 是 B	
S (MTA) (Neg) V₁ O₁ 跟/和 (Neg) V₂ O₂ A 跟/和 B (Time When) 都　(Neg) V O	

1. 你今天上午有中文課嗎？昨天呢？

_____

2. 你星期一下午有課嗎？星期二跟星期三呢？

_____

3. 我們今天有功課嗎？明天呢？

_____

4. 你們哪一天不上課？(Saturday and Sunday, use 也)

_____

5. _____

他昨天晚上做功課，今天晚上也做功課。

3. The possessive verb 有 — choice-type (A-not-A) form

S（MTA）有沒有 O？	有， S （MTA） 有 O
S（MTA）有 O 沒有？	沒有，S （MTA）沒(有) O

1. Q1:_____ Q2:_____
    小高有中國朋友。

2. Q1:_____ Q2:_____
    小李今天沒有中文課。

3. Q1:_____ Q2:_____
    我們今天有功課。

4. The question word 什麼／甚麼

S MTA 有什麼 N?	S MTA 有 N/NP
S MTA 上什麼課?	S MTA 上 X 課
S MTA 做什麼?	S MTA VO

1. 你後天有什麼課？

_____

2. 你明天上午上什麼課？

_____

3. 你星期五晚上做什麼？

_____

5. The question word 幾

S MTA 有 幾 M N?	S MTA 有 No. M N

1. _____

   他有三個中國朋友。

2. _____

   她今天有一堂課。

3. _____

   我星期四有三門課 (three courses)。

6. The auxiliary verb 得

S MTA 得 V O 嗎？ (AuxV)	對, S MTA 得 V O 不, S MTA 不必 V O 不, S MTA 不用 V O

1. 你今天得預備功課嗎？

   _____

2. 你星期五下午得上課嗎？

   _____

3. 你週末得打工嗎？

   _____

Ⓑ Usage of Common Phrases

1. X 也是 expression

S₁ MTA V O S₂ 也是	S₁ Time V O S₂ too

1. With your limited language skill, sometimes you may just want to be a copy cat.

   他昨天上中文課。→

   他有三個中國朋友。→

   她這個學期(xuéqī 'semester')有四門課。→

IV. Listening

1. Which is true about the dialogue?
    a.   B has classes on Tuesday and Thursday afternoons.
    b.   B has classes on Tuesday and Thursday mornings.
    c.   B has classes on Monday and Friday mornings.
    d.   B has classes on Monday and Thursday mornings.

2. Which is true about the dialogue?
    a.   B has to work on Saturdays and Sundays.
    b.   B has to prepare for his homework on Saturdays and Sundays.
    c.   B has to prepare for his homework on Saturdays, but has to work on Sundays.
    d.   B has to work on Saturdays, but has to prepare for his homework on Sundays

3. Which is true about Xiao Li's schedule?
    a.   He has no classes today, nor tomorrow or the day after tomorrow.
    b.   He has no classes today, but two classes tomorrow.
    c.   He has a Chinese class today and a Japanese class tomorrow.
    d.   He has two classes the day after tomorrow.

4. Which statement is true according to the dialogue?
    a.   Xiao Gao has three classes per week.
    b.   Xiao Gao has English classes on Tuesday only.
    c.   Xiao Gao has Chinese classes on Monday, Wednesday, and Friday.
    d.   Xiao Gao has no classes on Tuesday and Thursday.

5. Listen to the dialogue and write down the class schedule for Xiao Lin.

	星期一	星期二	星期三	星期四	星期五
上午					
下午					

 V. Speaking

A. Talk about yourself
    Use the following questions as cues.

    1.   你一三五有課嗎？二四有沒有課？

2. 你今天上午有什麼課？下午有什麼課？

3. 你一個星期有幾堂課？

4. 你打工嗎？哪一天得打工？

B. Schedule a get-together
Use the schedule you filled out in Vocabulary C (p. 20) to talk with a partner and find out if you take similar courses and can arrange to get together for a study group.

C. Recite the following children's song to practice numbers with measure words.

Yì zhī qīngwā yì zhāng zuǐ, liǎng .ge
　yǎn.jīng, sì tiáo tuǐ
Liǎng zhī qīngwā, liǎng zhāng zuǐ, sì .ge
　yǎn.jīng, bā tiáo tuǐ
Pīngpīngpāngpāng tiàoxià shuǐ, hámǎ bù
　chī shuǐ, tàipíng nián, hámǎ bù chī
　shuǐ, tàipíng nián.

一隻青蛙一張嘴，兩個眼睛，四條腿

兩隻青蛙兩張嘴，四個眼睛，八條腿

乒乒乓乓跳下水，蛤蟆不吃水，太平年

，蛤蟆不吃水，太平年。

One frog, one mouth, two eyes, four legs,
Two frogs, two mouths, four eyes, eight legs,
They jumped into the water one by one.
It would be peaceful if they won't drink water.
It would be peaceful if they won't drink water.

VI. Reading

A. Read the Text
Check your comprehension of the lesson dialogue by answering the following questions.

1. Xiǎo Gāo jīn.tiān shàng.wǔ yǒu shén.me kè?
Xià.wǔ yǒu jǐ táng kè?

小高今天上午有什麼課？下午有幾堂課？

_____

2. Xiǎo Gāo tiān.tiān dōu yǒu kè .ma?

小高天天都有課嗎？

_____

3. Xiǎo Lǐ něi yì tiān yǒu kè?   小李哪一天有課？

_____

4. Xiǎo Gāo zhōumò zuò shén.me?   小高週末做什麼？

_____

5. Xiǎo Lǐ xīngqītiān xiū.xī .ma?   小李星期天休息嗎？

_____

B. Read the Journal
    Read the journal and choose the correct answer accordingly.

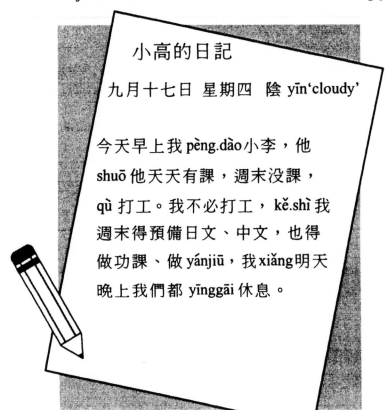

小高的日記

九月十七日　星期四　陰 yīn 'cloudy'

今天早上我 pèng.dào 小李，他
shuō 他天天有課，週末没課，
qù 打工。我不必打工，kě.shì 我
週末得預備日文、中文，也得
做功課、做 yánjiū，我 xiǎng 明天
晚上我們都 yīnggāi 休息。

New Words:
pèng.dào	to run into
shuō	to say
qù	to go
kě.shì	but
yánjiū	research
xiǎng	to think
yīnggāi	should; ought to

_____ 1. Xiao Gao is thinking about (a) what to do on Friday evening, (b) what to do
          during the weekends, (c) how to prepare for his research.

_____ 2. Xiao Gao feels that (a) he needs to find a part-time job, (b) he needs to prepare
          for his Chinese and Japanese classes, (c) he needs to take a break once in a while.

_____ 3. Xiao Li has to (a) work full-time, (b) go to classes Monday through Friday, (c) do
          his homework on weekends.

C. Read the Authentic Material

1. Read the following card distributed by the Hong Kong travelers' association and their hotline. Figure out when one can call them.

_____

_____

_____

香港萬事通旅遊熱線
服務時間

星期一至五：上午九時至下午五時
星期六：　　上午九時至中午十二時四十五分（香港）
　　　　　　上午九時至中午十二時（台北）

逢星期日及國定假日，請利用錄音留言。

香港旅遊協會

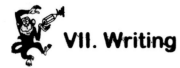

VII. Writing

A. Write the pinyin and the tone marks for the following and translate them into English.

1. 我每天早上都有中文課。

2. 他週末得打工和預備功課。

3. 我們今天不必做功課嗎？

B. Complete the paragraph by filling in the appropriate words with their corresponding number.

Hints   1.得   2.節   3.也   4.跟   5.都   6.和   7.不必

我的朋友每天早上＿＿＿有課。我每天早上＿＿＿都有課。他上中文課，

我上日文課。我二、四上午也＿＿＿上英文課。他不必上英文課，他得

打工＿＿＿預備功課。我＿＿＿他每個星期都有七＿＿＿課。

C. Rearrange the following words into meaningful sentences.

1. 做功課／都／她／晚上／得／朋友／每天／的。

2. 什麼／下午／上／你／今天／課？

3. 有／我們／也／上午／中文課／每天／都。

D. Complete the following dialogue.

A: ＿＿＿＿＿＿＿＿＿＿＿＿＿＿＿＿＿＿＿＿＿＿＿ 1

B: 沒有，我二、四沒課。

A: ＿＿＿＿＿＿＿＿＿＿＿＿＿＿＿＿＿＿＿＿＿＿＿ 2

B: 對了，我一、三、五有課。

A: ＿＿＿＿＿＿＿＿＿＿＿＿＿＿＿＿＿＿＿＿＿＿＿ 3

B: 我上三堂課，中文、日文、和英文。

A: ＿＿＿＿＿＿＿＿＿＿＿＿＿＿＿＿＿＿＿＿＿＿＿ 4

B: 我週末休息。

第六課　你上哪兒去？

 I. Vocabulary

A. Guess the right word/phrases for the following contexts.

1. You say ____ when you stepped on someone's toes.
2. You say ____ when you congratulate someone for his/her birthday.
3. You say ____ to greet your friend on the street.
4. You say ____ when you want to inquire the general state of your friend.
5. You say ____ when you feel things (e.g., your courses) are going fine.
6. You say ____ when you want to elicit your friend's opinion after relating your own.

a.	nǐ .ne	你呢
b.	zàijiàn	再見
c.	Duì.buqǐ	對不起
d.	shàng nǎr qù	上哪兒去
e.	zěn.meyàng	怎麼樣
f.	búcuò	不錯
g.	búbì	不必
h.	shén.me	什麼
i.	zhù nǐ shēng.rì kuàilè	祝你生日 快樂

B. Complete the crossword puzzle with the cues given.

				1		
		2				
						3
			4	5		
6						

Across	**Down**
1. credit	1. semester
2. Friday	3. this morning
3. this year	4. library
5. every day	
6. a bookstore	

C. Choose the appropriate word to complete the following sentences.

1. Zhè .ge xuéqī wǒ xuǎn .le liù mén kè, gōngkè hěn (lèi, zhòng, hǎo).

這個學期我選了六門課，功課很（累、重、好）。

2. (Zěn.meyàng, Nǎr, Duì.buqǐ), xiànzài jǐ diǎn jǐ fēn?

（怎麼樣、哪兒、對不起），現在幾點幾分？

3. Tā (yǐ.jīng, hěn, hái.shì) dàsān .le, (bútài, kě.shì, kuàiyào) hái méi.yǒu juédìng tā .de zhuānyè.

他（已經、很、還是）大三了，（不太、可是、快要）還沒有決定他的專業。

II. Characters

Hàn zì	去	到	書	店	好	得	買	了	誰	很
Notes	qù to go 5	dào arrive 8	shū book 10	diàn store 8	hǎo good 8	dé, děi to obtain 11	mǎi to buy 12	liǎo .le to finish 2	shéi who 15	hěn very 9
1										
2										
3										
4										
5										
6										

	Compound/Phrase/Sentence/Memory Aid
去	
到	
書	
店	
好	
得	
買	
了	
誰	
很	

Hàn zì	太	忙	多	少	快	要	點	分	這	兒
Notes	tài excessive 4	máng busy 6	duō much 6	shǎo few 4	kuài fast 7	yào to want 9	diǎn a little 17	fēn minute 4	zhè this 11	ér child 8
1										
2										
3										
4										
5										
6										

	Compound/Phrase/Sentence/Memory Aid
太	
忙	
多	
少	
快	
要	
點	
分	
這	
兒	

SVO

III. Grammar

🅐 Major Sentence Patterns

1. The aspect marker 了

1.1 Completed action with 了

S V 了 O 嗎？	Did S V O?
S V 了 O 沒有？	Has S V-ed O?
S V 了 O（了）	S did V O
S 還沒 V（O）呢！	S hasn't V-ed O yet

Answer the following questions based on information in the checklist.

1. 我今天上了中文課沒有？

   _____

2. 我買了書沒有？

   _____

3. 我不喜歡什麼課？我退了那門
   課沒有？

   _____

Done	• dropped French course
	• registration
	• signed up for three courses
	• did Chinese homework
To Do	• buy Chinese books
	• check out a Japanese book
	• decide a major
	• work part-time

4. 我註了冊嗎？選了課沒有？這個學期選了幾門課？

   _____

1.2 Change status with 了

S V O 了嗎？	Has S V-ed O?
S V O 了沒有？	
S 已經 V（O）了	S has already V-ed O
S 還沒 V（O）呢！	S hasn't V-ed O yet

1. 你們開學了沒有？

   _____

2. 書店關門了嗎？

   _____

3. 現在幾點鐘了？

_____

4. 今天是幾月幾號了？ (I have not yet done my homework.)

_____

5. 她們是大學生嗎？ (They were not college students last year.)

_____

1.3 Imminent action with 了

S 快要 V(O) 了	S is about to V O

1. 圖書館快要關門了嗎？

_____

2. 她們快要上小學了嗎？

_____

3. 他快要十六歲 (suì 'year old') 了嗎？ (He can get a driver's license soon.)

_____

2. V...來/去 construction

2.1 Questions with question words 哪兒 and 什麼地方

S (MTA)(要)上/到哪兒　　來/去？	S (MTA)(要)上/到 Place 來/去
上/到甚麼地方來/去？	S (MTA)　　上/到 Place 來/去了

1. 你明年要上哪兒去？

_____

2. 你昨天下午到什麼地方去了？

_____

3. 你喜歡哪兒？什麼時候上那兒去？

_____

2.2 Questions with particle 嗎

S (MTA)要 上/到 Place 來/去 嗎 ？	S (MTA)(不)要 上/到 Place 來/去
S (MTA) 上/到 Place 來/去 了嗎 ？	S (MTA) 上/到 Place 來/去了
	S (MTA) 没 上/到 Place 來/去

1. 你上個月上芝加哥(Zhījiāgē 'Chicago')去了嗎 ？

   _____

2. 你明天要到圖書館去嗎 ？

   _____

3. 你下個星期要上我家來嗎 ？

   _____

3. V...來/去 VO construction

S (MTA)   (要)上/到 Place 來/去 VO 嗎 ？
S (MTA) (不)(要)上/到 Place 來/去 VO
S (MTA) (没)   上/到 Place 來/去 VO

Answer the following questions based on the information provided in Xiao Gao's long-range plan.

1. 小高去年到哪兒去 ？

   _____

When	Where	What
前年	中國	玩兒
去年	日本	學日文
今年	美國	學日文
明年	中國	學中文
後年	臺灣	教英文

2. 他明年要到中國去做什麼 ？

   _____

3. 他後年要做什麼 ？

   _____

4. 他前年到日本去學日文了嗎 ？

   _____

4. Time when expressions

S 幾點鐘 V (O)?	S Time When V (O)
S 甚麼時候 V (O)?	

Answer the following questions with information from Xiao Li's daily schedule.

When	Where	What
上午	學校	上課
中午	書店	買書
下午1:00	圖書館	打工
下午3:00	圖書館	學習
晚上	宿舍	休息

1. 小李什麼時候要上書店去買書？

　　_____

2. 他上午要到學校去做什麼？

　　_____

3. 他幾點鐘要上圖書館去打工？

　　_____

4. 他晚上要到圖書館去借書嗎？

　　_____

5. A 還是 B construction

S （AuxV） V O₁ 還是 VO₂ (呢)?	S （AuxV） V (O)
S （AuxV） V A 還是 B　（呢)?	S （AuxV） V A/ S V B

1. _____

我決定主修中文。

2. _____

我要買中文書，不要買日文書。

3. _____

我退了日文課、也退了法文課。

Ⓑ Usage of Common Phrases

1. Telling the time by the clock

O'clock		Quarter	Minute	Second
點(鐘)	(零)/過/差	刻	分	秒

What time is it now?

　1. _____　　2. _____　　3. _____

2. 上、下、這 in time expressions

Gloss	Year	Month	Week	Weekend	Day
Last	去年	上個月	上個星期	上個週末	昨天
This	今年	這個月	這個星期	這個週末	今天
Next	明年	下個月	下個星期	下個週末	明天

Look at my monthly planner to answer the questions.

1. 我＿＿＿＿＿＿＿ 借書，＿＿＿＿＿＿＿還書。

2. 我＿＿＿＿＿＿退了日文課，＿＿＿＿＿＿加選中文。

3. 我 ＿＿＿＿＿＿ 決定主修中文，＿＿＿＿＿＿上中國去。

4. 我 ＿＿＿＿＿＿ 打工 ，＿＿＿＿＿＿ 也打工 。

1997   My Major: Chinese

	星期日	星期一	星期二	星期三	星期四	星期五	星期六
九月	18	19 退日文	20	21	22	23	24 打工
	25	26	27 借書	㉘今天	29 加選中文	30	31
十月	1	2	3	4	5	6 買電腦	7 打工
	8 Apply to the Study Abroad program '98	9	10 還書	11	12	13	14

 # IV. Listening

1. Where and what is B going to do?
   a. B is going to the library to borrow a book.
   b. B is going to the library to return a book.
   c. B is going to the bookstore to buy a book.
   d. B is going to the bookstore to buy a notebook.

2. What is B's major?
   a. Chinese
   b. Japanese
   c. International Business
   d. Library Science

3. When will the library close?
   a. Six o'clock.
   b. Eight o'clock.
   c. Five o'clock.
   d. Nine o'clock.

4. Which is true about Xiao Li's courses?
   a. His course load is too heavy so he decided to drop the Japanese course.
   b. He took four courses and sixteen credits this semester.
   c. His course load is too heavy so he decided to drop the Japanese and French courses.
   d. He has decided to take two courses only.

5. Which statements are true about the dialogue?
   a. Xiao Gao is going to the library to prepare for his classes next week.
   b. Xiao Li is going to the bookstore to buy some books.
   c. Xiao Li is going to the library to check out some books.
   d. Xiao Gao is going to buy some books so he can start preparing for his courses.

6. You are Xiao Li's roommate. Listen to the following comments he made about different courses and answer the questions.
   a. What does Xiao Li think of the French course?
   b. What does Xiao Li think of the Japanese course?
   c. Which language course did he decide to take? Why?

V. Speaking

A. Talk about yourself
   Use the following questions as cues.
   1. 你主修什麼？你的專業是什麼？你副修什麼？

   2. 你這學期的課重不重？修了幾門課？多少個學分？

   3. 你喜歡中文課嗎？你喜歡你的中文書嗎？你每天幾點上中文課？

   4. 你什麼時候要到中國去念書？

B. Time management
   Write down your daily schedule (作息表 zuòxíbiǎo) using the chart on the next page and discuss it with a partner to see how you can better manage your time.

Sample: A: 你幾點鐘 VO？
B: 我六點十分 VO.

Vocabulary in context:

qǐchuáng	to get up
chī zǎofàn	to have breakfast
zhōngfàn	lunch
wǎnfàn	dinner
tīng lùyīn	to listen to tapes
duàn.liàn	to work out
xǐzǎo	to take a bath
shuìjiào	to go to bed

Time	Activity

C Find a partner in your class and talk to each other about your major, the credits you are taking this semester, and the textbooks you have bought.

D. Find out the library's hours and tell a new student who wants to know when the library will be open.

E. Find out the store hours of your favorite bookstore and tell your friend about it.

VI. Reading

A. Read the Text
Check your comprehension of the lesson dialogue by completing the following sentences:

1. Gāo Dézhōng yào shàng _____ qù
    _____ .

    高德中要上_____去_____。

2. Lǐ Míng yào dào _____ qù _____ .

    李明要到_____去_____。

3. Lǐ Míng jiāxuǎn .le _____ kè, tuì .le
    _____ kè.

    李明加選了____課，退了____課。

4. Lǐ Míng jué.de (think) Rìwénkè
    _____ .

    李明覺得日文課_____。

5. Gāo Dézhōng jué.de zhè .ge xuéqī .de kè
    _____. Tā xuǎn .le ____ kè, ____ .ge
    xuéfēn.

高德中覺得這個學期的課_____
。他選了____課、____個學分。

6. Lǐ Míng juédìng zhǔxiū _____, fùxiū
    _____.

李明決定主修____，副修____。

7. Lǐ Míng yào gēn Gāo Dézhōng shuō
    "zàijiàn," yīn.wéi (because)
    _____.

李明要跟高德中說「再見」，因爲
_____。

B. Read the Authentic Material
    Read the Chinese restaurant's advertisement and find out the store hours.
    1. The store is open on_____

    2. The store is closed on _____

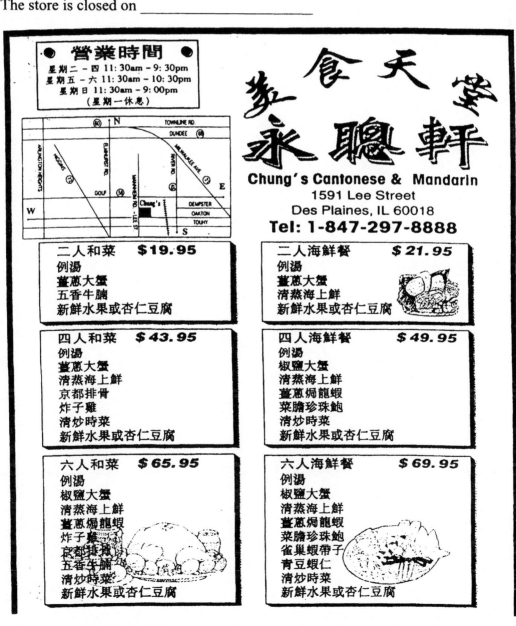

VII. Writing

A. Write the Chinese characters for the following sentences in pinyin and translate them into English.

1. Nǐ shàng nǎr qù?

2. Tā xué Zhōngwén gēn Rìrén, tiān.tiān dōu hěn máng, hěn lèi.

3. Wǒ míng.tiān xià.wǔ yào dào shūdiàn qù mǎi jǐ běn shū.

B. Rearrange the following words into meaningful sentences.

1. 到／你／七點(鐘)／上午／去／哪兒／了

2. 五點(鐘)／書／來／買／要／這兒／他

3. 你／什麼／了／選(xuǎn)／課／今年

C. Complete the dialogue using the cues provided.

A: 小李，＿＿＿＿＿＿＿＿＿＿＿＿＿＿？₁

B: 我上圖書館去。

A: ＿＿＿＿＿＿＿＿＿＿＿＿＿＿＿？ (to do what) ₂

B: ＿＿＿＿＿＿＿＿＿＿＿＿＿＿. (to check out some books) ₃

A: 你下午沒課嗎？

B: 沒有，＿＿＿＿＿＿＿＿＿＿＿＿＿＿＿＿＿.₄
　　　(attended three classes in the morning and need to work on the homework now.)

D. Translate the following sentences into Chinese

1. A: What did you do this morning?

    B: I withdrew from the Japanese course and added Chinese.

2. A: Excuse me, what time is it now?

   B: It's already fifteen minutes pass six. The bookstore is closed.

3. A: The library is about to open. You need to go there to prepare for your classes on Monday.

   B: But I'm too tired now and I also need to work (part-time) this afternoon.

4. A: Have you done your homework yet?

   B: Not yet, but I've already studied.

E. Writing and Sharing
Write a passage in Chinese describing how many courses and credits you are taking, and whether you like your courses or not. Do not write down your name. The teacher will shuffle the writings, read them aloud in class, and have students guess who wrote what.

第七課 一共多少錢？

I. Vocabulary

A. Think of things that have two qualities from the following word list.

lǎo	老
jiù	舊
guì	貴
pián.yí	便宜
kuài	快
hǎokàn	好看
hǎochī	好吃

1. 什麼東西又貴又快？（又… 又 yòu...yòu 'both...and...'）

   _____

2. 什麼東西又便宜又好看？

   _____

3. 什麼東西又好看又好吃？

   _____

B. Write the pinyin and the meaning of the items on the following list and tell your classmate where they are located in your room/house. (e.g., 電腦在我的桌上。)

1. 電腦　_____　_____
2. 本子　_____　_____
3. 筆　_____　_____
4. 錄音帶　_____　_____
5. 隨身聽　_____　_____
6. 字典　_____　_____
7. 光碟　_____　_____
8. 咖啡

C. Choose the appropriate word to complete the following sentences.

1. Wǒ shēn.shàng méi.yǒu qián, (zǎojiù, zhǐhǎo, yǐ.jīng) huíjiā.　我身上沒有錢，（早就、只好、已經）回家。

2. Nèi běn shū (méicuò, bù pián.yí, búcuò), kě.shì yào sānshí kuài.　那本書（沒錯、不便宜、不錯），可是要三十塊。

3. (Qǐngtīng, Qǐngwèn, Qǐngshuō) zhè yí.ge yào (jǐ, nǎ xiē, duō.shǎo) qián?　（請聽、請問、請說）這一個要（幾、哪些、多少）錢？

II. Characters

Hàn zì	請	問	説	坐	可	以	看	完	先	吃
Notes	qǐng please 15	wèn to ask 11	shuō to speak 14	zuò to sit 7	kě may, able 5	yǐ by means of 5	kàn to see 9	wán to finish 7	xiān first 6	chī to eat 6
1										
2										
3										
4										
5										
6										

	Compound/Phrase/Sentence/Memory Aid
請	
問	
説	
坐	
可	
以	
看	
完	
先	
吃	

Hàn zì	飯	吧	再	給	東	西	才	就	在	那
Notes	fàn food 12	.ba particle 7	zài again 6	gěi to give 12	dōng east 8	xī west 6	cái only, then 3	jiù then 12	zài in, at, etc. 6	nà that 7
1										
2										
3										
4										
5										
6										

	Compound/Phrase/Sentence/Memory Aid
飯	
吧	
再	
給	
東	
西	
才	
就	
在	
那	

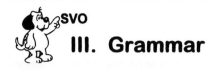

III. Grammar

❶ Major Sentence Patterns

1. Place words

Pron /N + localizer

Draw a line to connect words between columns one and two and give their meaning in English.

他	家	
我們	那兒	
她們	這兒	
學生	宿舍	

2. The main verb 在

S　(MTA) 在 哪兒/什麼地方？	S　(MTA)　 在 Place
S　(MTA) 在不在 Place？	S　(MTA)不在 Place
S　(MTA) 在 Place 嗎？	

Take a look at Xiao Gao's living quarters and answer the questions accordingly.

1. 他的本子在不在桌子(zhuō.zi 'desk')上 (on the desk)？

   _____

2. 什麼東西在書上 (on top of the books)？

   _____

3. 他的字典在什麼地方？

   _____

4. 他的朋友在他那兒嗎 ？

   _____

3. The existential verb 有

Place 有沒有 X?	Is there X at Place?
Place 有 X	There is X at Place
Place 沒有 X	There is no X at Place

1. _____

小高的桌上有書，有很多書。

2. _____

小高那兒沒有朋友。

3. _____

小高的桌上有一個隨身聽。

4. The adverb 就

X 就在 Place	X is right over at Place
才 No. M 就要 No. 塊(錢)	(It's) only No. M and (it) costs No. dollars
早就... 了	(It) has already...

1. 你的電腦在哪兒 ？(right there)

    _____

2. 那本書(200 pages) 貴不貴 ？

    _____

    $79.99

3. 你的三明治吃完了沒有 ？

    _____

4. 你字典買了沒有 ？

    _____

5. 先 ...再 construction

S 先 V_1O_1 ，再 V_2O_2	S will V_1O_1 first, (and) then V_2O_2

1. 你每天晚上做些什麼 ？(take a rest and do homework)

    _____

2. 你每天早上做些什麼 ？(drink coffee and come to school)

    _____

3. 你明年要到哪兒去？(through Japan to China)

_____

4. 你下個月要上哪兒去？(through San Francisco to LA)

_____

6. Resultative verbs — actual form

V + RE 完 + 了	finished Ving
(還) 沒 V + RE 完 (呢)	(still) haven't finished Ving (yet)

1. 你學完了第五課沒有？

_____

2. 你聽完了這一課的錄音帶沒有？

_____

3. 你吃完了中飯 (zhōngfàn 'lunch') 沒有？

_____

4. 你做完了今天的功課沒有？

_____

B Usage of Common Phrases

1. Compounds vs. noun phrases

Monosyllabic Adj + N	Compound noun	Adj N
(Adv) + Adj + 的 + N	Noun phrase	The N that/which is Adj
Disyllabic Adj + 的 + N	Noun pharase	The N that/which is Adj
Polysyllabic Adj + 的 + N	Noun pharase	The N that/which are Adj

Take turns modifying the following nouns and see how long you can go.

e.g. 書→舊書→很舊的書→一本很舊的書

1. 電腦_____

2. 宿舍_____

3. 隨身聽_____

2. The adverbial phrase 一點兒

Adj 一點兒	a little bit Adj-er
有一點兒 SV	(is) a little bit too Adj

$2,000

1. 你覺得這個電腦貴不貴？(a bit expensive/Where can I get a cheaper one?)

_____

_____

2. 你覺得這部車怎麼樣？(a bit old/Do you have cars that are slightly newer?)

_____

3. 你覺得你們的功課多不多？(a bit too much/Please give us less homework.)

_____

3. 多少錢 expression

N, 一 M 多少錢？	(N), 一 M No. $

1. 在中國，一盤磁帶多少錢？一本書呢？

_____

2. 在美國，一個隨身聽多少錢？在台灣呢？

_____

3. 書店的筆，一枝多少錢？

_____

4. V 一下 expression

V（一）V	just VO
V 一下	just VO

1. 你累了嗎？

    對，_____

2. 你要喝這杯咖啡嗎？

　　好，＿＿＿＿＿＿＿＿＿＿＿＿＿＿＿＿＿＿＿＿＿＿

3. 你要買這個電腦嗎？(just take a look)

　　不，＿＿＿＿＿＿＿＿＿＿＿＿＿＿＿＿＿＿＿＿＿＿＿

4. 你明天有中文課嗎？(need to prepare)

　　對，＿＿＿＿＿＿＿＿＿＿＿＿＿＿＿＿＿＿＿＿＿＿＿

5. The agreement particle 吧

好吧！	O.K.!

Translate the following dialogues between A and B, who take turns making suggestions and giving consent.

1. A: Let's go to the library. B: OK.

　　A:＿＿＿＿＿＿＿＿＿＿＿＿＿＿＿＿＿＿＿　B:＿＿＿＿＿＿＿＿

2. A: Let's have a cup of coffee. B: Fine.

　　A:＿＿＿＿＿＿＿＿＿＿＿＿＿＿＿＿＿＿＿　B:＿＿＿＿＿＿＿＿

3. A: Please come to my place tomorrow, all right?   B: All right.

　　A:＿＿＿＿＿＿＿＿＿＿＿＿＿＿＿＿＿＿＿　B:＿＿＿＿＿＿＿＿

 ## IV. Listening

1. How much is the novel?
   a. $20.40
   b. $10.50
   c. $30.50
   d. $10.60

2. Which is true about Xiao Gao?
   a. Xiao Gao has a computer.
   b. Xiao Gao doesn't have a computer because he doesn't like it.
   c. Xiao Gao cannot afford to buy it.
   d. Xiao Gao doesn't need a computer.

3. What does A want to buy?
    a. a book.
    b. a novel.
    c. a dictionary.
    d. a notebook.

4. How much is the tape?
    a. $5.30
    b. $3.50
    c. $4.50
    d. $5.50

 # V. Speaking

A. Talk about yourself
    Use the following questions as cues.
    1. 你喜歡上書店去買東西嗎？你喜歡上哪一家書店去買東西？

    2. 你最近(zuìjìn 'recently')在書店買了什麼東西？那些東西貴不貴？

    3. 你最近(zuìjìn 'recently')看了小說沒有？看了什麼小說？

    4. 你喜歡喝咖啡嗎？你一天喝幾杯咖啡？

    5. 你喜歡吃中國飯還是美國飯（漢堡、三明治）？

B. Find a partner and take turns playing customer and salesperson. Refer to the following
    price list and:
    1. Ask the salesperson about the prices of the items on the list.
    2. Tell the salesperson that you would like to buy five items (of your choice); don't forget to
        use appropriate measure word for each item.
    3. Ask how much is the total.

中文字典	中文字典	Zhōngwén zìdiǎn	$17.30
英文字典	英文字典	Yīngwén zìdiǎn	$14.99
中國小說	中国小说	Zhōng.guó xiǎoshuō	$20.50
本子	本子	běn.zi	$1.50
毛筆	毛笔	máobǐ	$5.00

錄音帶	录音带	lùyīndài	$2.99
隨身聽	随身听	suíshēntīng	$48.99
光碟	光碟	guāngdié	$16.99
咖啡	咖啡	kāfēi	$.99

VI. Reading

A. Check your comprehension of the lesson dialogue by deciding whether the statements are true or false.

T / F 1. Lǐ Míng zhǐ yào mǎi yì běn shū.
李明只要買一本書。

T / F 2. Lǐ Míng méi.yǒu qián, suǒ.yǐ mǎi .le yì běn jiùshū.
李明沒有錢，所以買了一本舊書。

T / F 3. Diànyuán shuō diàn .lǐ zhǐ (only) yǒu xīn .de "Zhōng.guó Xiǎoshuō."
店員說店裏只有新的「中國小說」。

T / F 4. Lǐ Míng xiān mǎi .le dōng.xī, fù (to pay) .le qián, zài hē kāfēi.
李明先買了東西，付了錢，再喝咖啡。

T / F 5. Lǐ Míng běnlái (originally) xiǎng qù chī Zhōng.guófàn.
李明本來想去吃中國飯。

T / F 6. Lǐ Míng hěn xǐ.huān chī sùshè .de hànbǎo sānmíngzhì.
李明很喜歡吃宿舍的漢堡、三明治。

T / F 7. Lǐ Míng mǎi .de dōng.xī yígòng yào yì bǎi duō kuài.
李明買的東西一共要一百多塊。

T / F 8. Lǐ Míng mǎi .le tài duō dōng.xī, suǒ.yǐ zuìhòu (at last) shēn.shàng zhǐ yǒu sān kuài qián.
李明買了太多東西，所以最後身上只有三塊錢。

B. Read the Authentic Material

　　1. Read the following advertisement and find out:

　　　　a. What is the name of the store?　　_____

　　　　b. What is the advertised item?　　_____

　　　　c. What is the price of this item?　　_____

波士頓 中國書店
TEL: (617)426-0888
FAX: (617)426-0208
使用信用卡(VISA, MASTER, AMEX)
可来電或 FAX 訂書
支票抬頭：Central China Book Co. Inc.
每次訂購另加郵費、保險費共$4.50
44 Kneeland St., Basement, Boston, MA 02111

英漢醫學大詞典
特價$48，香港版，精裝硬皮大 32 開本，繁體字，原價$84

　　2. Read the following advertisement and find out:

　　　　a. What is the name of the store?　　_____

　　　　b. What kind of items does this store sale?　　_____

　　　　　　_____

　　　　c. Can you figure out other information?　　_____

　　　　　　_____

密西根州
大底特律
世界書局
※台灣大陸圖書/期刊/暢銷書/郵票
※國際特廉電話卡/文具/禮品/卡片
※錄影帶英語教學/無敵電子翻譯機
※台港 CD 卡拉 OK 鐳射片/各類錄音帶
歡迎光臨
歡迎郵購・接受信用卡
電話：(810)585-6007
地址：30805 John R Rd.
　　　Madison Hgts. MI 48071

　　3. Read the following charts on exchange rate and find out:

　　　　a. How many Hong Kong dollars can you exchange for $300 人民幣？_____

　　　　b. How many 人民幣 will you get for 200 US dollars? _____

c. What is the exchange rate between Taiwanese dollars and British pound?_____

5 月 26 日

中間價 人民幣兌外幣	外幣名稱	中間價
	100 美元	829. 23
	100 日圓	7. 1845
	100 港幣	107. 17

台幣外匯匯率表 (5月30日)

幣別	買入	賣出
美元	27.83	27.93
德國馬克	16.32	16.52
英鎊	45.50	45.90
瑞士法郎	19.65	19.85
日圓	0.2376	0.2416
澳幣	21.22	21.42
加拿大幣	20.12	20.32
法國法郎	4.81	4.91
港幣	3.565	3.625
新加坡幣	19.39	19.59
南非幣	6.18	6.36
馬來西亞幣	11.01	11.19
泰國銖	1.097	1.117

VII. Writing

A. Rearrange the following words into meaningful sentences.

1. 書架／錄音帶／哪兒／在／不
　　jià　　lùyīndài

2. 中國小說／看完／那本／還沒／我／呢
　　　shuō　　wán　　　　　hái

3. 貴／書店／的／他們／書／有一點兒
　guì　　　　　　　　　　　　diǎnr

4. 再／咖啡／他／喝完／先／做功課
　　zài　kāfēi　　　　wán　xiān　zuò gōngkè

B. Complete the following paragraph by filling in the blanks.

我昨天上午到大學的圖書館去＿＿＿＿₁，看了一＿＿＿＿₂中文小說，

我覺得很＿＿＿＿₃，可是我沒＿＿＿＿₄。那本書一共兩百多頁，我就

看了五十頁。我太累了，決定回家＿＿＿＿₅，明天下午再去看。

C. Translate the following sentences into English and order them into a coherent passage.

1. 考 kǎo 'test' 完期中考，我要休息一下，看看印大 Yìndà 'IU' 的校園 xiàoyuán 'campus'。

　　＿＿＿＿＿＿＿＿＿＿＿＿＿＿＿＿＿＿＿＿＿＿＿＿＿＿＿＿＿＿＿＿＿＿＿

2. 我很累，可是還得念很多書，因為 yīnwèi 'because' 星期一要考期中考。

　　＿＿＿＿＿＿＿＿＿＿＿＿＿＿＿＿＿＿＿＿＿＿＿＿＿＿＿＿＿＿＿＿＿＿＿

3. 星期 xīngqī 天晚 wǎn 上我回布城 Bùchéng 來。

　　＿＿＿＿＿＿＿＿＿＿＿＿＿＿＿＿＿＿＿＿＿＿＿＿＿＿＿＿＿＿＿＿＿＿＿

4. 我家在普渡 Pǔdù 大學那兒。

　　＿＿＿＿＿＿＿＿＿＿＿＿＿＿＿＿＿＿＿＿＿＿＿＿＿＿＿＿＿＿＿＿＿＿＿

5. 因為印大校園很好看，這個星期很多葉子 yè.zi 'leaves' 都紅 hóng 'red' 了。

　　＿＿＿＿＿＿＿＿＿＿＿＿＿＿＿＿＿＿＿＿＿＿＿＿＿＿＿＿＿＿＿＿＿＿＿

6. 上個週末 zhōumò，我不在學校 xiào，我回家去了。

　　＿＿＿＿＿＿＿＿＿＿＿＿＿＿＿＿＿＿＿＿＿＿＿＿＿＿＿＿＿＿＿＿＿＿＿

7. The correct order for a coherent passage is: ＿＿＿＿＿＿＿＿＿＿＿＿＿＿＿＿＿

D. Imagine that you are running out of money and want to ask your parents to send you a check. You need to write a passage in Chinese describing how many books you have bought for the classes that you are taking now and how much each book costs. (Refer to the Supplementary Vocabulary of Lesson 6 for the names of the subjects.)

親愛的爸爸媽媽： Qīng'ài .de bà.ba mā.ma 'Dear parents'

　　　　我沒有錢了。

第八課　你認識她嗎？

I. Vocabulary

A. Write the antonyms of the following words. Provide pinyin and their English meanings.

1. hǎotīng　好聽　↔ _____　_____
2. guì　　　貴　　↔ _____　_____
3. nánkàn　難看　↔ _____　_____
4. ǎi　　　　矮　　↔ _____　_____
5. jiù　　　　舊　　↔ _____　_____
6. nán　　　難　　↔ _____　_____
7. huā shíjiān　花時間　↔ _____　_____
8. nánchī　　難吃　↔ _____　_____

B. In which country/region is the city located?

1. Xi'an　　　　　中國西部
2. Shanghai　　　_____
3. Chicago　　　　_____
4. San Francisco　_____
5. New York　　　_____
6. Paris　　　　　_____
7. Berlin　　　　　_____
8. Los Angeles　　_____

C. Choose the appropriate words to complete the following paragraph.

我喜歡(聲調、音樂)₁，覺得(小提琴、小說)₂很好聽，很想學(寫、
拉、做)₃提琴。(雖然、而是、不過)₄聽說拉琴(不一樣、不錯、不
容易)₅，也很花時間。我想我(不應該、不必、得)₆花太多時間，因
爲這個學期我已經選了四門課，而且'besides'我的專業不是音樂。

II. Characters

Hàn zì	老	師	姓	高	名	字	叫	美	想	走
Notes	lǎo old 6	shī teacher 10	xìng surname 8	gāo tall, high 10	míng name 6	zì a word 6	jiào to call 12	měi beautiful 9	xiǎng to think 13	zǒu to walk 7
1										
2										
3										
4										
5										
6										

	Compound/Phrase/Sentence/Memory Aid
老	
師	
姓	
高	
名	
字	
叫	
美	
想	
走	

Hàn zì	過	來	正	從	因	爲	但	而	怎	樣
Notes	guò to go by 13	lái to come 8	zhèng just…ing 5	cóng from 11	yīn a reason 6	wéi,wèi because 9	dàn but 7	é and, also 6	zěn how, why 9	yàng kind, sort 15
1										
2										
3										
4										
5										
6										

	Compound/Phrase/Sentence/Memory Aid
過	
來	
正	
從	
因	
爲	
但	
而	
怎	
樣	

SVO

III. Grammar

Ⓐ Major Sentence Patterns

1. 是...的 construction

S (是) Prep Phrase V O 的。	It is/was Prep Phrase that S V O
S (是) 從 Place₁ (到 Place₂) 來的。	It was from Place₁ that S came to Place₂
S (是) Time When (從 Place₁) (到 Place₂) 來的。	It was Time When that S came (from Place₁ to Place₂).

1. 你是從哪兒來的？

   _____

2. 你是什麼時候到這兒來的？

   _____

3. 你是來這兒做什麼的？

   _____

4. 你是幾點鐘上課的？

   _____

2. A 不是 X, 也不是 Y, 而是 Z

A 不是 X, 也不是 Y, 而是 Z	A is not X, nor is (it) Y; (it) is Z

1. 他是德國人還是英國人？

   _____

   2. 她是美國人還是法國人？

   _____

3. 他姓王還是姓李？

   _____

4. 你喜歡德國車還是美國車？

_____

3. **Adj 倒是(不) Adj, 可是...**

X,　　Adj 倒是(不) Adj, 可是 ...	As for X, it's (not) Adj, but ...
Topic ｜　　　Comment	

1. 你覺得中文難不難啊？

_____

2. 你覺得你的老師嚴不嚴啊？

_____

3. 你覺得這個大學好不好啊？

_____

4. **The progressive aspect marker 在**

S (正)在 VO (呢)	S is (in the midst of) Ving O

1. 她正在做什麼呢？

_____

2. 那個人正在做什麼呢？

_____

3. 這個學生正在做什麼呢？

_____

5. **雖然..., 可是/不過/但是... construction**

S 雖然..., 可是/不過/但是(S) ... 雖然 S ..., 可是/不過/但是(S)...	Although S..., but ...

1. 你喜歡吃中國飯嗎 ?

_____

2. 你覺得漢字難寫不難寫 ?

_____

3. 你要買電腦嗎 ?

_____

6. The movable adverb 爲什麼

S 爲什麼 V O ? 爲什麼 S V O ?	Why do(es)/did S V O ?

1. 你爲什麼要學中文 ?

_____

2. 你爲什麼昨天沒來上課 ?

_____

3. 你爲什麼要主修 X (your major) ?

_____

7. The auxiliary verb 想

S (不) 想 VO S 想 [A 不/沒 VO]	S (doesn't/don't) want(s) to VO S doesn't/didn't think that A VO

1. 你想聽中國音樂嗎 ?

_____

2. 你想小高喜不喜歡他的中文課 ?

_____

3. 你想他有沒有錢 ?

_____

4. 你想他明天來不來？

_____

8. 不是...嗎？ expression

S 不是 V O 嗎？ 不是 S V O 嗎？	Isn't it true that S V O？

1. 我覺得很累。(You took a break this morning, didn't you?)

_____

2. 我想喝杯咖啡。(Isn't it true that you don't drink coffee?)

_____

3. 我的聲調不太好。(Isn't it true that you practice tones every day?)

_____

Ⓑ Usage of Common Phrases

1. The verbs 姓、叫

您貴姓？/S 姓什麼？	S 姓 X
S 姓 / 叫 (EV) 什麼名字？	S 叫 X
S 姓 / 叫 X 嗎？	S 姓 / 叫 X 不，S 不(是)姓 / 叫 X

Imagine a dialogue between A and B with the information provided on the name cards.

A: _____

B: 我姓林，你呢？

A: _____

中美圖書公司
林大成
Executive
Tel:(123)456-7890　123 Main Street, Suite 45
Fax:(123)456-7890　Big City, State, USA 12345

西北大學
李思明
Professor
Depart. of Music
phone: 782-0139
fax: 782-0233

2. The optional possessive marker 的

Pron + (的) + kinship term	Possessive Pron + kinship term
Pron + (的) + 家/ 學校/宿舍	Possessive Pron + home/school/dormitory

Which of the following 的 are optional? _____

1. 他認識我的媽媽。

2. 他的電腦非常快。

3. 他的女朋友很好看。

4. 我們的家有四個人。

5. 你的筆多少錢？

3. 像…一樣 expression

[S V (O)], 像X一樣	[S V (O)]; (It) seems/sounds/looks like X

1. 上中文課累不累？打工累不累？

   _____

2. 聽中文錄音帶有沒有意思？聽音樂有沒有意思？

   _____

3. 學中文容易不容易？像學什麼一樣？

   _____

4. Verb-object construction

[VO]ₙ + Adv + SV	[Ving O] is Adv Adj

Imagine you are the mayor of a city called_____(name it in Chinese). You want to find out how people feel about doing various activities in this place. Conduct the following survey.

1. 在 _____，做什麼很難？→_____

2. 做什麼很有意思？→_____

3. 做什麼很花時間？→_____

4. 做什麼很花錢？→_____

5. 做什麼很容易？→_____

IV. Listening

1. Which is true about A and B?
   a. They are old friends.
   b. They are classmates.
   c. They are meeting for the first time.
   d. They are good friends.

2. Where did B's friend come from?
   a. Eastern part of China.
   b. Western part of China.
   c. Southern part of China.
   d. Northern part of China.

3. How is B's Chinese teacher?
   a. She is very strict.
   b. She is not very strict.
   c. She is very easygoing.
   d. She is very nice.

4. Are Chinese characters hard to write?
   a. They are not too hard to write.
   b. They are very hard to write.
   c. They are quite easy to write.
   d. They are too hard to write.

 V. Speaking

A. Talk about yourself
   Use the following questions as cues.
   1. 你叫什麼名字？請你說一下你的中文名字(identify each character)。

   2. 你現在在學什麼？那門課/那個專業難不難？為什麼？

   3. 你覺得你的老師怎麼樣？

   4. 你喜歡音樂嗎？你拉不拉小提琴(or any other instrument)？

B. Introduce one of your friends to your classmates. Remember to mention (1) his/her name and the meaning of the name, (2) place of origin, (3) occupation, and (4) hobbies and special talents, e.g., playing any musical instruments.

C. Find a partner to role play the following situations.
A new student asks for your advice on taking certain courses. You want to help out by providing as much detailed information as possible about the teacher (name, place of origin, etc.), way of teaching (strict, demanding, etc.) and course load (a lot of homework and readings). Include your personal reaction to the course (you like it, hate it, etc.).

VI. Reading

A. Read the Text
Check your comprehension of the lesson dialogue by answering the following questions.

1. Shì shéi jiè.shào Xiǎo Gāo rè.shì Xiǎo Lín .de?   是誰介紹小高認識小林的？

_____

2. Xiǎo Gāo hé Lín Měiyīng shì cóng nǎr lái .de?   小高和林美英是從哪兒來的？

_____

3. Lín Měiyīng zěn.me (how) jiè.shào zìjǐ (self)?   林美英怎麼介紹自己？

_____

4. Gāo Dézhōng .de fùmǔ shì něiguó rén??   高德中的父母是哪國人？

_____

5. Wèishén.me Xiǎo Lǐ shuō Xiǎo Lín hé Xiǎo Gāo   為什麼小李說小林和小高走在
zǒu zài yíkuàir chéng .le Liánhéguó .le?   一塊兒就成了聯合國了？

_____

6. Gāo Dézhōng zài xué shén.me? Tā jué.de nèi   高德中在學什麼？他覺得那門
mén kè nán .bùnán?   課難不難？

_____

7. Lín Měiyīng xǐ.huān zuò shén.me?   林美英喜歡做什麼？

_____

8. Měiyīng wèishén.me jué.de zìjǐ xué Zhōngwén yīnggāi méi wèntí?

美英為什麼覺得自己學中文應該沒問題？

_____

9. Gāo Dézhōng jué.de tā .de Zhōngwén lǎoshī zěn.meyàng?

高德中覺得他的中文老師怎麼樣？

_____

B. Read the Authentic Material
　1. Read the advertisement on the right and figure out what it is about.

_____
_____
_____
_____
_____

2. Read the advertisement on the left and figure out:

　a. What is it about?

_____

　b. How many days a week is this company/store open?

_____

VII. Writing

A. Rearrange the following into meaningful sentences.

1. 有一點兒／中文／難／可是／很喜歡／我
    diǎr   nán

2. 他／美國人／不是／日本人／中國人／也不是／而是
                                                    ér

3. 很有意思／可是／很花時間／雖然／寫漢字
    yì.sì   huā shíjiān suírán

B. Imagine that you are a journalist and need to confirm the following overheard statements by raising specific questions.

1. 他是一九九四年從中國到美國來的。
    a. Question concerning *when*

    b. Question concerning *from where*

    c. Question concerning *to where*

2. 我是去年從美國到日本去學日文的。
    a. Question concerning *when*

    b. Question concerning *from where*

    c. Question concerning *to where*

C. Write a passage in Chinese to introduce an imaginary figure or a character of your choice. Do not reveal the name before your teacher reads your work aloud in class and has others guess who you are writing about.

_____

_____

_____

_____

第九課 請問你打幾號？

I. Vocabulary

A. Write a word that contains the same character or radical as the previous one and see how long you can build your word-train.

e.g., 門→門口→吃飯→中國飯→中文→英文

1. 做飯→＿＿＿＿＿→＿＿＿＿＿→＿＿＿＿＿→＿＿＿＿＿→＿＿＿＿＿

2. 打電話→＿＿＿＿＿→＿＿＿＿＿→＿＿＿＿＿→＿＿＿＿＿→＿＿＿＿＿

3. 作文→＿＿＿＿＿→＿＿＿＿＿→＿＿＿＿＿→＿＿＿＿＿→＿＿＿＿＿

B. Complete the crossword puzzle with the cues given.

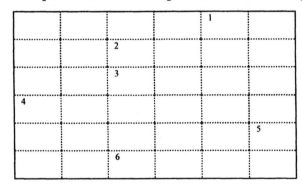

Across	Down
2. what time?	1. take time
4. read Chinese books	3. composition class
6. do it yourself	4. go to movies
	5. occupied

C. Choose the appropriate word to complete the following sentences.

1. Wǒ (shuō, kàn, děng) nǐ bú huì Zhōngwén, érqiě méi.yǒu Zhōng.guó péng.yǒu, (hái.shì, hái, ér.shì) yǐhòu zài shàng Zhōng.guó qù .ba.

   我（說、看、等）你不會中文，而且沒有中國朋友，（還是、還、而是）以後再上中國去吧。

2. Tā suīrán shì Měi.guórén, dàn.shì Zhōng .guóhuà shuō .de hěn (hǎotīng, róng.yì, dì.dào).

   他雖然是美國人，但是中國話說得很（好聽、容易、地道）。

3. Zuò Zhōng.guófàn (bú tài nán, tǐng má.fán, hǎo jí .le), érqiě yào huā hěn duō shíjiān.

   做中國飯（不太難、挺麻煩、好極了），而且要花很多時間。

II. Characters

Hàn zì	打	工	電	話	找	出	時	間	咱	們
Notes	dǎ beat 5	gōng work 3	diàn electricity 13	huà words 13	zhǎo to look for 7	chū to go out 5	shí time 10	jiān M 12	zá I, me 9	.men plural ending 10
1										
2										
3										
4										
5										
6										

	Compound/Phrase/Sentence/Memory Aid
打	
工	
電	
話	
找	
出	
時	
間	
咱	
們	

Hàn zì	作	事	前	後	能	見	半	和	對	起
Notes	zuò to do 7	shì job 8	qián before 9	hòu after 9	néng can 10	jiàn see 7	bàn half 5	hé and, with 8	duì correct 14	qǐ get up 10
1										
2										
3										
4										
5										
6										

	Compound/Phrase/Sentence/Memory Aid
作	
事	
前	
後	
能	
見	
半	
和	
對	
起	

SVO

III. Grammar

❶ Major Sentence Patterns

1. The co-verb 給

A 沒/要　給　B V　O A　　　給　B V 了 O	Co-verb	A didn't/will V O to B A did V O to B
A 沒/要　V O　給　B A　　　V 了 O 給 B A　　　V 了 O 給 B 了	Marker of indirect object construction	A didn't/will V O to B A did V　O to B A has V-ed O to B

1. 你昨天給誰打了電話？

　　_____

2. 你媽媽每天給你做什麼？

　　_____

3. 你明天得寫信(xìn 'letter')給誰？

　　_____

4. 你朋友上個月買了什麼給你？

　　_____

2. … 以前/以後 expressions

Time Expression/ VO + 以前,… (reference point)	Before Time Expression/Ving O, …
Time Expression　 + 以後,… 　　V 了/ 完 O + 以後,… (reference point)	After Time Expression, … After finishing VingO, …

Answer the following questions based on the information provided in the chart.

1. 我今天什麼時候有空兒？

　　_____

2. 我每天什麼時候聽錄音？(before…)

　　_____

我	昨天	今天
9:00	上語言實驗室聽錄音	
10:10	上日文課	上日文課
1:30	去圖書館	打工
5:45	回家	回家
7:00	寫漢字	做功課
8:00		
10:00	休息	

3. 我昨天什麼時候去圖書館？(before...)

_____

4. 我今天什麼時候回家？(after...)

_____

3. The preposition 在

在...V	S (Time When) 在 Place V(O)	S V (O) at Place (Time When)
V 在...	S (Time When) V 在 Place	S V at/on/in Place (Time When)

1. 你每天都在哪兒念書？

_____

2. 你每天都在哪兒練習聲調 ？

_____

3. 他喜歡坐在哪兒？

_____

4. 他喜歡躺(tǎng 'to lie on back')在哪兒 ？

_____

4. 從 ... 到 ... 來 /去 construction

S Time When 從 Place₁ 到 Place₂ 來 /去	S is/was coming/going from Place₁ to Place₂ at/on Time When

1. 他什麼時候從中國到美國布城來？

_____

2. 他一九九六年從哪兒到哪兒去 ？

_____

Résumé Timeline	
1990	Beijing
1993	Shanghai
1994	Bloomington
1996	Boston, New York
1997	Hong Kong, Japan

3. 他今年(1997)要從哪兒到哪兒去？

_____

5. The adverb 才

S Time When 才 V (O)	S won't V (O) until Time When
S V₁了 O 才 V₂ (O)	S won't V₂ (O) until finishing doing V₁O

1. 我今天七點鐘吃早飯嗎？

_____

2. 我預備六點半回家嗎？

_____

3. 我今天十二點鐘休息嗎？

_____

My Schedule	
8:00	eat breakfast←**NOW**
9:30	go to the library to
10:10	go to Chinese class
12:00	have lunch
1:15	have a break
2:00	go to classes
5:30	go to the lab
7:00	go home

4. 我現在要上圖書館去嗎？

_____

6. Resultative verbs — potential form

Question	V 得 RE 不 RE?	can ... V or not?
Affirmative form	V 得 RE	can V...
Negative form	V(得)不 RE	cannot V...

1. 你中文說得好不好？

_____

2. 你媽媽飯做得怎麼樣？

_____

3. 你唱歌唱得好不好？

_____

7. Topicalization

O,　　　S　V/RV Topic,　　comment S,　　　O　V/RV	As for O, S (can/cannot) V…

Rewrite the following in topic-comment structure to emphasize the objects.

1. 他每天都要喝三杯咖啡。→

_____

2. 我覺得你應該天天練習聲調。→

_____

3. 我不認識他的中文老師，但是我聽說他很不錯。→

_____

ⓑ Usage of Common Phrases

1. The adverbial phrase 一塊兒

A 跟 B Vᵢ 在一塊兒	A and B Vᵢ together
A 跟 B 一塊兒 V (O)	A and B V(O) together

1. 你每天跟誰一塊兒做功課？

_____

2. 你每天跟誰一塊兒學中文？

3. 他跟誰走在一塊兒？

_____

2. 請 vs. 問

A 請 B VO	A invites/asks B to VO
A 問 B X	A asks B about X

1. 昨天我(請、問)我的朋友今天來我家吃飯。我(請、問)他能不能六點鐘來，他說他五點四十五分才下課。他(請、問)我等他一下，他下課以後馬上 (mǎshàng 'immediately') 來。

3. The auxiliary verbs 可以、能 、會

S　(不) 可以/能/會 V O	S may/can/will (not) V O
可以	may, to be permitted to, it is all right to; can
能	may, to be permitted to = 可以; can, is able to (in terms of capability)
會	can, to know how to; will, could possibly or would probably

1. 我的美國朋友很有意思。他很(可以 、會)說中國話，但是不(能、會)寫漢字。明年他(會、可以)到中國去，但是他沒有錢。我說他(會、可以)在中國教英文，他說他不(能、會)，因為教英文太花時間。他已經沒有錢了，不(會、能)再沒有時間。他說：「時間就是錢啊！」

4. 看 for expressing opinions

你 看… 怎麼樣？	How about …?
你 看…嗎？/ …V-not-V…？	Do you think …?/ Will …or not ?
我 看 X...	I think (in my opinion) X...

1. 你看咱們下課以後去喝咖啡，怎麼樣 ？ (decline with an excuse)

_____

2. 咱們明天下午出去看電影兒，好嗎 ？ (accept with an alternate time)

_____

3. 我們找他出去吃飯，好不好 ？ (He won't go with us.)

_____

5. The particle …好了

咱們 VO 好了	Let's just VO
你　　VO 好了	Why don't you just VO

1. 那門課很重。 (Drop it.)

_____

2. 這兒的東西貴極了！(Let's go to another store to shop.)

_____

3. 你跟我一塊兒上圖書館去吧！(You go by yourself.)

_____

4. 我想跟她一塊兒去看電影兒。(Give her a call.)

_____

 # IV. Listening

1. Why did Xiao Chen call Xiao Zhang?
   a. Xiao Chen wants to do homework with Xiao Zhang.
   b. Xiao Chen wants to invite Xiao Zhang to have dinner.
   c. Xiao Chen wants to invite Xiao Zhang to go to a movie.
   d. Xiao Chen wants to invite Xiao Zhang to have dinner and to go to a movie.

2. Where and when are Xiao Chen and Xiao Zhang going to meet?
   a. At the entrance to their school at 7:30 p.m.
   b. At the entrance to their school at 1:30 p.m.
   c. At the entrance to their dorm at 7:30 p.m.
   d. At the entrance to their dorm at 1:30 p.m.

3. Which is true about the dialogue?
   a. Xiao Wang and Xiao Lin are going to invite Xiao Li and Xiao Gao to eat out.
   b. Xiao Wang and Xiao Lin are going to invite Xiao Li and Xiao Gao to have dinner at home.
   c. Xiao Wang and Xiao Lin are going to invite Xiao Li and Xiao Gao to cook for them.
   d. Xiao Wang and Xiao Lin are going to Xiao Li and Xiao Gao's place for dinner.

4. Listen to the phone message recorded on your answering machine and try to figure out what it is about.

_____

_____

_____

V. Speaking

A. Talk about yourself
   Use the following questions as cues.
   1. 你喜歡給朋友寫信還是打電話？爲什麼？

   2. 你每個星期什麼時候有空兒？什麼時候請朋友吃飯？

   3. 你喜歡出去吃飯還是在家吃飯？爲什麼？

   4. 你覺得美國的中國飯地道嗎？爲什麼？

B. Star Search
   Interview your classmates with the following form to find out what talents they have and how well they handle the skills, e.g., 你會說什麼話？你＿＿話說得怎麼樣？

	Name	Skill	Excellent	Good	Fair
1.					
2.					
3.					
4.					
5.					
6.					
7.					
8.					

C. What Is It?
   Think of a common object (e.g., a telephone, a Chinese meal) and have your classmates guess what it is by asking questions such as:

   那個東西可以吃嗎？

   那個東西能不能看？

   那個東西會不會說話？

   那個東西圖書館有沒有？

D. Make a Phone Call
   1. Call your friend and ask her/him to go to the library to study Chinese with you.

2. Make a phone call to your classmate and ask him/her to come to your house to cook a meal together. Pretend that you only know how to make Chinese food, while s/he only knows how to make American food, and that you want to learn from each other.

3. Your friend calls you to invite you to have dinner this weekend, but you have to work and do your homework. Decline the invitation with an apology.

4. Phone your teacher and let him or her know that you cannot come to class this Friday. You have to go home for a special family dinner because it is your father's birthday.

VI. Reading

A. Read the Text

Check your comprehension of the lesson dialogue by deciding whether the statements are true or false.

T / F   1.   Gāo Dézhōng yào gěi Wáng Huá, 　　高德中要給王華、美英打電話。
             Měiyīng dǎ diànhuà.

T / F   2.   Gāo Dézhōng dǎcuò yí.cì (once) 　　高德中打錯一次電話。
             diànhuà.

T / F   3.   Wáng Huá rèn.shì (to know) Gāo 　　王華認識高德中。
             Dézhōng.

T / F   4.   Gāo Dézhōng xiǎng zhǎo Měiyīng, 　高德中想找美英、李明星期五出
             Lǐ Míng xīngqīwǔ chū.qù chīfàn, 　去吃飯、看電影。
             kàn diànyǐng.

T / F   5.   Měiyīng shuō tā bù néng gēn Gāo 　美英說她不能跟高德中出去吃飯
             Dézhōng chū.qù chīfàn, yīn.wèi tā 　，因為她有課。
             yǒu kè.

T / F   6.   Lín Měiyīng bù xǐ.huān chū.qù chīfàn, 林美英不喜歡出去吃飯，因為出
             yīn.wèi chū.qù chīfàn tài guì .le. 　去吃飯太貴了。

T / F   7.   Gāo Dézhōng xǐ.huān chū.qù 　　高德中喜歡出去吃飯，因為做飯
             chīfàn, yīn.wèi zuòfàn tài máfán .le. 太麻煩了。

T / F   8.   Gāo Dézhōng jué.dé zìjǐ hěn huì
diǎn (order) Zhōng.guócài.

高德中覺得自己很會點中
國菜。

T / F   9.   Lín Měiyīng Zhōng.guófàn zuò .de
hěn hǎo, suǒ.yǐ tā yào zìjǐ zuòfàn.

林美英中國飯做得很好，所以她
要自己做飯。

B. Read the Authentic Material
   1. Read the following advertisement, and find out
      a. The phone rate for China: _____

      b. The phone rate for Hong Kong (香港 Xiānggǎng):_____

      c. The phone rate for Taiwan (臺灣 Táiwān): _____

      d. Is there any restriction on when and where one can make a phone call? _____

2. If you want to use a credit card to make a phone call, which public phone should you use ? _____

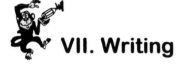

VII. Writing

A. Rearrange the following into meaningful sentences.

1. 圖書館／以後／他／寫完字／到…去／借書
   tú　guǎn　yǐhòu　　　　wán　　　　jiè

2. 我／以前／吃飯／咖啡／喝了／兩杯
   yǐqián　　kāfēi　　　　bēi

3. 學校／都／他／在／每天／做功課
   xiào　　　　měi　　gōng

4. 九點鐘／小林／學校／到／要／才
   zhōng　　　　　　　　　cái

5. 我／一塊兒／想／吃飯／他／跟／小王／去／請
   kuàir　xiǎng　　　　　　wáng

B. Translate the letter on the right as best as you can for your Chinese friend, who does not know English well.

> October 15, 1997
>
> Hi, Xiao Zhang:
>
> How are you doing? This month I have been very busy, but I still made a lot of phone calls to my parents. I've missed them very much since I've come here. Last week my father bought me a violin and my mother bought me a Chinese book. Do you cook American food for yourself now? Write me after you finish your computer course.
>
> Lili (your friend)

C. Write down the phone messages you took for your roommate while s/he was out.

1.

Date 10/15/97

Time 11:45 (AM) PM

M Mike Lin   ☐ URGENT

Of _____ ☐ Phoned

Phone (   ) 855-5789   ☐ Returned
                                Your Call

Message want to go to the movie   ☒ Will Call
with you   Again

....
....
....
....
....
....
....
....

2. Jane Lee called around 4:30
    this afternoon to invite you for
    dinner tomorrow. She asked
    you to return her call when
    you get back.

Message For

_____

_____

While you were out _____

_____

_____

_____

_____

_____

_____

_____

_____

_____

_____

第十課　我們吃什麼好呢？

I. Vocabulary

A. Match the pictures with the appropriate new words.

1.

4.

kǎoyā	烤鴨
niúròu	牛肉
jī	雞
chē	車
qìshuǐr	汽水兒
píjiǔ	啤酒
yú	魚

2.

5.

3.

6.

B. Write other words with the same meaning in pinyin and English.

1. shì.yíshì　試一試　＝　___shì.yíxià___　　___to try___
2. dàjiā　　　大家　　＝　_____　_____
3. kǒuwèir　　口味兒　＝　_____　_____
4. xīyān　　　吸煙　　＝　_____　_____
5. diǎncài　　點菜　　＝　_____　_____

C. Choose the appropriate word to complete the following sentences.

1. Zhè jiā fànguǎn .de cài dōu búcuò, hǎixiān (hái.shì, bǐjiào, tèbié) hǎochī.

這家飯館的菜都不錯，海鮮（還是、比較、特別）好吃。

2. Nǐ xiǎng .bù xiǎng hē píjiǔ? (Hǎo.le, Suàn.le, Duì.le) jīn.tiān wǒ děi kāichē.

你想不想喝啤酒？（好了、算了、對了）今天我得開車。

3. Qǐng nǐ gěi wǒ xiān lái diǎnr chūnjuǎn, bāo.zi, (zěn.meyàng, shén.me .de, yīn.wèi), wǒ è jí .le.

請你給我先來點兒春捲、包子、（怎麼樣、什麼的、因為），我餓極了。

4. Nǐ.men yígòng jiào .le jǐ (hú, táng, dào) cài?

你們一共叫了幾（壺、堂、道）菜？

II. Characters

Hàn zì	菜	館	喝	著	湯	水	魚	肉	喜	歡
Notes	cài vegetable 12	guǎn a house 16	hē to drink 12	.zhe suffix 12	tāng soup 12	shuǐ water 4	yú fish 11	ròu meat 6	xǐ rejoice 12	huān joyous 22
1										
2										
3										
4										
5										
6										

	Compound/Phrase/Sentence/Memory Aid
菜	
館	
喝	
著	
湯	
水	
魚	
肉	
喜	
歡	

Hàn zì	茶	酒	南	北	方	比	開	車	錯	重
Notes	chá tea 10	jiǔ wine 10	nán south 9	běi north 5	fāng direction 4	bǐ to compare 4	kāi to open 12	chē vehicle 7	cuò error 16	chóng again 9
1										
2										
3										
4										
5										
6										

	Compound/Phrase/Sentence/Memory Aid
茶	
酒	
南	
北	
方	
比	
開	
車	
錯	
重	

III. Grammar

A Major Sentence Patterns

1. V 得 Adj construction

S V O V 得 (Adv) Adj	S V (very/quite) Adj O
S O V 得 (Adv) Adj	
S V O V 得 不 (Adv) Adj	S cannot V Adj O
S O V 得 不 (Adv) Adj	

1. 你會不會包 'to wrap' 餃子？你包得怎麼樣？

_____

2. 你是北方人嗎？北方菜做得怎麼樣？

_____

3. 你會不會開車？開車開得怎麼樣？

_____

2. Comparative constructions

2.1 Explicit comparison

A 比 B Adj 嗎？	Is A Adj-er than B
A 比 B Adj	A is Adj-er than B
A 比 B Adj（得)多了	A is much more Adj-er than B
A 比 B Adj 一點兒	A is a little bit Adj-er than B
A 不比 B Adj	A is not as Adj as B

1. 中國菜口味比日本菜重嗎？(a little bit)

_____

2. 德國車比美國車貴嗎？(much more)

_____

3. 中文比英文難嗎？(much more)

_____

2.2 Implicit comparison

(A 跟 B),哪M (比較) Adj?	(As for A and B), which one is Adj-er?
A （比較） Adj	A is Adj-er
A Adj (得)多了	A is much more Adj
A Adj 一點兒	A is a little bit more Adj

1. 你覺得牛肉跟魚，哪個好吃？

   _____

2. 你覺得日本車跟美國車，哪個好開？ (a little bit)

   _____

3. 你覺得美國電影跟中國電影，哪個好看？(much more)

   _____

2.3 Equaling-degree comparison

A有沒有 B (這麼 / 那麼) Adj？	Is A as Adj as B?
A 　　有 B (這麼 / 那麼) Adj	A is as Adj as B
A 　沒有 B (這麼 / 那麼) Adj	A is not as Adj as B

1. 中文有沒有日文那麼難學？

   _____

2. 魚湯有沒有雞湯這麼好喝？

   _____

3. 南方人有北方人那麼高嗎？

   _____

2.4 Equal-degree comparison

A 　跟 B 　一樣 Adj 嗎？	Are A and B equally Adj？
A 　跟 B 　　一樣 Adj	A and B are equally Adj
A 　跟 B 不一樣 Adj	A and B are not equally Adj
A不跟 B 　　一樣 Adj	A is not equally Adj with B.

1. 春捲跟餃子一樣好吃嗎？

   _____

2. 這家飯館跟那家一樣貴嗎？(MacDonald vs. Red Lobster)

   _____

3. _____

   北方菜口味沒有南方菜重。

3. ... 的 N construction

S V 的 O	The O that S V

1. 你做的菜，怎麼樣？

   _____

2. 他給你介紹的朋友好不好？

   _____

3. 你認識的中國人多不多？

   _____

4. The soup that my mother made is very delicious.

   _____

5. The books that he wrote are all very interesting.

   _____

6. I like to listen to the songs that she sang.

   _____

7. I don't like the fish that Xiao Wang made.

   _____

8. I cannot understand what (the things that) he said.

   _____

4. The experiential aspect marker 過

S 　　V 過　O 嗎？	Have S ever done ...(before)?
S 沒 V 過　O 嗎？	Hasn't S done... (before)?
V 過　　　 /S 　　　V 過 O	S has done ... (before)
還沒 V 過 /S 還沒 V 過 O	S hasn't done... yet

1. 你吃過春捲嗎？

＿＿＿＿＿＿＿＿＿＿＿＿＿＿＿＿＿＿＿＿

2. 你開過日本車嗎？你覺得日本車怎麼樣？

＿＿＿＿＿＿＿＿＿＿＿＿＿＿＿＿＿＿＿＿

3. 你看過中國電影嗎？覺得中國電影怎麼樣？

＿＿＿＿＿＿＿＿＿＿＿＿＿＿＿＿＿＿＿＿

5. The progressive aspect marker 著

S （正）V 著　O（呢）	S is (in the midst of) Ving O
S 　　　V 著（O）V(O)	S V (O) while Ving (O)

1. 他在做什麼呢？

＿＿＿＿＿＿＿＿＿＿＿＿＿＿＿＿＿＿＿＿

2. 你喜歡喝著咖啡做什麼？

＿＿＿＿＿＿＿＿＿＿＿＿＿＿＿＿＿＿＿＿

3. 中國人跟朋友出去吃飯，是一個人叫一道菜還是大家分著吃？

＿＿＿＿＿＿＿＿＿＿＿＿＿＿＿＿＿＿＿＿

❸ Usage of Common Phrases

1. The suggestion particle 吧

(S) 來（一）M N（吧）	Let (S) have N!
(S) 來（一）點兒 N（吧）	How about having/ordering N?

Look at the menu and order your lunch.

1. 你身上只有五塊錢，你非常餓。

＿＿＿＿＿＿＿＿＿＿＿＿＿＿＿＿

Menu			
漢堡	大漢堡	魚漢堡	雞塊
$2.19	$2.48	$2.70	$6.99
三明治	桔子水	可口可樂	咖啡
$2.99	$.99	$.89	$.70

2. 你不吃牛肉。

_____

2. A 對 B 好

A 對 B (Adv) 好	A is (Adv) good/nice for/to B
VO 對 B (Adv) 好	Ving O is (Adv) good for/to B
A 對 B 不 (Adv) 好	A is not (Adv) good/nice for/to B
VO 對 B 不 (Adv) 好	Ving O is not (Adv) good for/to B

1. 誰對你很不錯？為什麼？

_____

2. 做什麼對身體很不好？

_____

3. 做什麼對學中文很好？

_____

 # IV. Listening

1. Why do Xiao Li and Xiao Gao want to eat out?
    a. Because they don't know how to cook.
    b. Because they don't have time to cook.
    c. Because their dorm doesn't serve dinner tonight.
    d. Because their dorm doesn't have enough food.

2. Why do they want to go to New Beijing restaurant?
    a. Because they like New Beijing's steam breads and chicken.
    b. Because they like New Beijing's dumplings and roast duck.
    c. Because they like New Beijing's steam bread and roast duck.
    d. Because they like New Beijing's noodles and chicken.

3. Where does the dialogue take place?
    a. At a bookstore.
    b. At a restaurant.
    c. At a theater.
    d. At a market.

4. Who is A?
   a. a salesperson.
   b. a student.
   c. a customer.
   d. a waiter/waitress.

5. How is Hunan's food?
   a. Their fish is not good, but their hot-sour soups and dumplings are delicious.
   b. Their fish and hot-sour soups are pretty good, but their dumplings are not good.
   c. Their fish and dumplings are delicious, but their hot-sour soups are not good.
   d. Their fish is delicious, but their hot-sour soups and dumplings are not good.

 # V. Speaking

A. Talk about yourself
   Use the following questions as cues.
   1. 你喜歡去什麼飯館兒吃飯？爲什麼？

   2. 你喜歡吃什麼口味的菜？你喜不喜歡吃辣的？

   3. 你吃不吃魚？什麼你不吃？

   4. 你吃過什麼特別(tèbié 'special')的菜？請你介紹一下。

B. Likes and dislikes
   Survey your classmates with the following form to find out what they like and dislike, e.g.,
   你喜歡看誰寫的小說？你喜歡吃誰做的飯？你喜歡開哪一國做的車？

	Name	Likes	Dislikes
1.			
2.			
3.			
4.			
5.			

C. Refer to the following information and discuss with your friend:

1. Which restaurant's food is better and more/less expensive;
2. Which food you like best.

湖南飯館的菜單

菜名	價錢
烤鴨 kǎoyā	$15.00
糖醋魚 tángcùyú	$12.00
酸甜肉 suāntiánròu	$9.00
芥蘭牛肉 jièlán niúròu	$10.00
宮保雞丁 gōngbǎo jīdīng	$8.00
青豆蝦仁 qīngdòu xiārén	$12.50
麻婆豆腐 mápó dòu.fù	$7.00
炒青菜 chǎo qīngcài	$6.00
春捲兒(一個) chūnjuǎnr	$1.00
餃子(十個) jiǎo.zi	$5.00
炒麵 chǎomiàn	$8.00
酸辣湯 suānlàtāng	$2.00
蛋花湯 dànhuātāng	$1.50
杏仁豆腐 xìngrén dòu.fù	$5.00
新鮮水果 xīnxiān shuǐguǒ	$5.50

長城飯館的菜單

菜名	價錢
烤鴨 Roast duck	$18.00
糖醋魚 Sweet & sour fish	$10.00
酸甜肉 Sweet & sour pork	$8.00
芥蘭牛肉 Beef with kale	$11.00
宮保雞丁 Gongbao chicken	$8.00
青豆蝦仁 Shrimp with peas	$14.50
麻婆豆腐 Mapo tofu	$7.50
炒青菜 Vegetables	$5.00
春捲兒(一個) Egg roll	$1.50
餃子(十個) Dumplings	$6.00
炒麵 Fried noodles	$7.00
酸辣湯 Hot-sour soup	$2.50
蛋花湯 Egg drop soup	$1.50
杏仁豆腐 Almond tofu	$4.00
新鮮水果 Fresh fruits	$4.50

VI. Reading

A. Read the Text
Check your comprehension of the lesson dialogue by answering the following questions.

1. Gāo Dézhōng xiǎng qù nǎ yì jiā fànguǎn
   chīfàn? Lǐ Míng .ne?　　　　　　　高德中想去哪一家飯館吃飯？李
   　　　　　　　　　　　　　　　　　明呢？

   _____

2. Lǐ Míng jué.de "Chángchéng" .de fàn
   zěn.meyàng? "Húnán" .de .ne?　　　李明覺得「長城」的飯怎麼樣？
   　　　　　　　　　　　　　　　　　「湖南」的呢？

   _____

3. Tā.men juédìng qù nǎ jiā chī? Wèishén.me?　他們決定去哪家飯館吃？爲什麼
   　　　　　　　　　　　　　　　　　？

   _____

4. Lǐ Míng wèishén.me shuō, "yì rén jiào yí
   dào cài hǎo .le?"　　　　　　　　　李明爲什麼說：「一人叫一道菜
   　　　　　　　　　　　　　　　　　好」了？

   _____

5. Lín Měiyīng bù chī shén.me? Tā jiào .le
   shén.me cài?　　　　　　　　　　　林美英不吃什麼？她叫了什麼菜
   　　　　　　　　　　　　　　　　　？

   _____

6. Gāo Dézhōng hé Lǐ Míng jiào .le shén.me
   cài?　　　　　　　　　　　　　　　高德中和李明叫了什麼菜？

   _____

7. Nǐ xiǎng Gāo Dézhōng xǐ.huān hǎixiān .ma?　你想高德中喜歡海鮮嗎？

   _____

8. Tā.men chī .le chūnjuǎn méi.yǒu?　　　他們吃了春捲沒有？

   _____

9. Tā.men hē .le shén.me? Wèishén.me?　　他們喝了什麼？爲什麼？

   _____

B. Read the Authentic Material

1. Read the following advertisement and figure out:

a. What is the name of this restaurant? _____

b. What kind of cuisine does this restaurant serve?_____

2. Read the following advertisement and figure out:

a. What kind of books are advertised? _____

b. How much are they? _____

c. How many characters can you recognize? (Circle the ones you know) _____

VII. Writing

A. Write about Xiao Gao, Xiao Li and Xiao Wang with the aid of the following questions and information.

	Height 身高 shēn'gāo	Weight 體重 tǐzhòng
小高	6ft 2in #chǐ #cùn	180 lb #bàng
小李	5ft 7in	145 lb
小王	5ft 8in	145 lb

1. Who is taller? Xiao Gao or Xiao Li?

2. Who is heavier? Xiao Gao or Xiao Wang?

3. Is Xiao Li as heavy as Xiao Wang?

B. Leave a note to your roommate who has asked you to bring something back for dinner. Tell him/her which dish you ordered and why. Your roommate prefers noodles to rice and especially likes roast duck. He is health-conscious and poor. Use the following questions and price list as an aid.

1. Which dish is more expensive? Roast duck or sweet-and-sour fish (tángcùyú)?

2. Is sweet-and-sour fish as expensive as the seafood with rice (海鮮飯)?

烤鴨	kǎoyā	$20.00
牛肉麵	niúròu miàn	$10.00
糖醋魚	tángcùyú	$12.00
海鮮飯	hǎixiānfàn	$12.00

3. Is beef noodle as expensive as sweet-and-sour fish?

C. Write a passage describing a unique place you have been to and you think your classmates may not know about. You will need to use experiential aspect marker 過 guò.

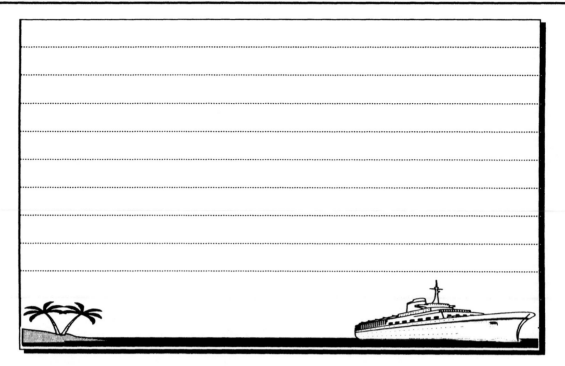

D. Reflect upon your own learning styles and take some notes. Are you a "multi-processing" person and prefer to listen to music while you study? Do you have any other peculiar study habits? You will need to use progressive aspect marker 著 zhe.

第十一 課 那部電影兒怎麼樣?

 I. Vocabulary

A. Describe the proper nouns in column one by connecting them with those in column two.

1	2	
1. Einstein	bēijù	悲劇
2. Lexus	xǐjù	喜劇
3. Tom Hanks	shū.fú	舒服
4. Hamlet	yánjiū	研究
5. Elizabeth Taylor	nányǎnyuán	男演員
6. Midsummer Night's Dream	nǚyǎnyuán	女演員

B. Write the meaning of the word and other vocabulary that you associate with it.

1. 麵包 __bread__ ≈ 牛奶、餓、吃東西、宿舍

2. 啤酒 _____ ≈ _____

3. 哭 _____ ≈ _____

4. 胃口 _____ ≈ _____

5. 漂亮 _____ ≈ _____

6. 感動 _____ ≈ _____

C. Choose the appropriate word to complete the following sentences.

1. Nǐ (cái, xiān, gāngcái) shàng nǎr qù .le? Wǒ
   zhǎo nǐ, nǐ bú zài.

   你(才、先、剛才)上哪兒去了?
   我找你,你不在。

2. Nǐ (méi, bié, bù) nánguò .le, xià yí.cì zài
   yònggōng yì diǎnr.

   你(沒、別、不)難過了,下一次
   再用功一點兒。

3. Kàn zhè běn shū (ràng, kě, bié) rén hěn lèi.

   看這本書(讓、可、別)人很累。

4. Zhōng.guórén (yíbànr, duōbànr, yígòng) dōu
   xǐ.huān hēchá.

   中國人(一半兒 6. 半兒、一共)都
   喜歡喝茶。

II. Characters

Hàn zì	牛	油	包	子	別	餓	男	女	自	己
Notes	niú ox, cow 4	yóu oil 8	bāo wrap 5	zǐ son, child 3	bié part, other 7	è hungry 15	nán male 7	nǚ female 3	zì self 6	jǐ self 3
1										
2										
3										
4										
5										
6										

	Compound/Phrase/Sentence/Memory Aid
牛	
油	
包	
子	
別	
餓	
男	
女	
自	
己	

Hàn zì	會	懂	所	談	真	像	每	次	最	近
Notes	huì can 13	dǒng understand 16	suǒ M 8	tán to talk 15	zhēn true 10	xiàng resemble 14	měi each 7	cì M for V 6	zuì the most 12	jìn close to 8
1										
2										
3										
4										
5										
6										

	Compound/Phrase/Sentence/Memory Aid
會	
懂	
所	
談	
真	
像	
每	
次	
最	
近	

SVO

III. Grammar

🅐 Major Sentence Patterns

1. 不是..., 就是 ... construction

不是 A, 就是 B	If it is not A, then it is B (It must be either A or B)

1. 你最近忙不忙？

  _____

2. 你每天早上都吃些什麼？

  _____

3. 你這幾天都上哪兒去念書？(library, my friend's place)

  _____

2. Frequency expressions

2.1 Do something no. of times per day/week/month/year

S 一/每 + 天/年 VO 幾次？ S 一/每 + 天/年 V 幾次O？ S 每 + No.+ 天/年 VO 幾次？ S 每 + No.+ 天/年 V 幾次O？	How many times does SVO a day/year? How many times does SVO per no. of days/years?
S 每 + (一)個 + 星期/月 VO 幾 次 ？ S 每 + (一)個 + 星期/月 V 幾次 O？ S (每)+ No. M N VO 幾次？ S (每)+ No. M N V 幾次O ？	How many times does SVO a week/month? How many times does SVO per no. of weeks/months/years?

1. 你一個月去看幾次電影？

  _____

2. 你一個星期打電話回家幾次？

  _____

3. 你每天都上圖書館去嗎？一天去幾次？

  _____

2.2 Did/have done something no. of times in the past/up to now

S V過　幾次　O？ O, S V過　幾次　？	How many times did S V O (in the past)? As for O, how many times did S V it (in the past)?
S V過　　幾次 O 了？ S V過 O 幾次　　了？ O, S V過幾次　　了？	How many times has S done VO (up to this moment)? As for O, how many times has S done V (up to thismoment)?

1. 你吃過日本飯沒有？吃過幾次了？

_____

2. 你看過中國電影嗎？中國電影你看過幾次了？

_____

3. 你聽過中國歌兒嗎？中國歌兒你聽過幾次了？

_____

2.3 Have never done X before

S　O 一次　也/都　沒V過 O, S 一次　也/都　沒V過	S has never done V O even once As for O, S has never done V O even once

1. 你阿拉斯加(Ālāsījiā 'Alaska') 去過幾次？

_____

2. 西藏 (Xīzàng 'Tibet') 飯你吃過幾次？

_____

3. 他肉吃過幾次？

vegetarian

_____

3. Manner or degree complements

S (O)　　V 得　SV-不-SV?	Does　S V (O)　Adv or not?
S (O)　　V 得　怎麼樣？	How does S V O?
S (VO) V 得　Adv SV	S V (O)　　　Adv　Adj
S (VO) V 得　不　SV	S V (O) not (Adv) Adj

1. 他的女朋友長得怎麼樣？

_____

2. 他的歌唱得好不好？

_____

3. 她電影演得怎麼樣？

_____

4. 要是..., 就... construction

S（要是）..., (S) 就... (MA)	If S..., (then) S...

1. 你要是很有錢，你要做什麼？

_____

2. 你喜歡吃什麼飯？要是你一個星期沒吃那個飯，你會覺得怎麼樣？

_____

3. 要是你很有名 'famous'，你會做什麼？

_____

5. 一點兒也/都 不 construction

S 一點兒也/都 不 AuxV (VO) O, S 一點兒也/都不 AuxV	S doesn't AuxV (VO) at all As for O, S doesn't AuxV at all

1. 你喜歡吃海鮮嗎？

_____

2. 你懂不懂「婦女研究」？

_____

3. 你明白不明白中國和台灣的關係？

_____

6. Question word 都(不)... construction

誰 ...	都(不)...	Everyone (No one)...
哪個人...	都(不)...	Everyone (No one)...

1. 誰想到中國(or other fun places) 去？

_____

2. 哪個人喜歡吃宿舍的飯？

_____

ⓑ Usage of Common Phrases

1. 上/ 這/ 下(一)次

which time?	哪(一)次？
last time	上(一)次
this/that time	這 (一)次/ 那(一)次
next time	下 (一)次

1. 你一個月看幾次電影？上一次看誰演的？下一次呢？

_____

2. 你去過芝加哥幾次？你覺得哪一次最有意思？

_____

3. 你這一次請吃飯，要請我們吃什麼？

_____

2. The prepositional phrase 在 ... 上

在 N/NP 上	In (the aspect of) ..., in terms of...

1. 在美國社會上，婦女的地位怎麼樣？

_____

2. 什麼人在中國社會上的地位很高？

_____

3.　喜福會這本小說在什麼上很特別？(in terms of language)

_____

3.　The superlative marker 最

Adj	很　Adj	更　　Adj	最　　　Adj
Adj	very Adj	even Adj-er	the most Adj./Adj-est

1.　最近什麼相當流行？

_____

2.　你覺得上哪兒去最好？

_____

3.　你覺得誰演的片子讓你最感動？

_____

4.　從這兒到芝加哥怎麼走最快？

_____

4.　好像...似的 expression

S 好像...似的	It seems that S...

1.　這個小朋友怎麼了？

_____

　　2.　這個人怎麼了？

_____

3.　他怎麼了？

_____

ⓒ Reentry

1. More on ...的 N construction

[S₂ V₂ 的 N]　SV₁ 　　　　　 S₁	[The N which S₂ V₂] to be Adj₁ 　　　　　 S₁
S₁ (AuxV) V₁　[S₂ V₂ 的 N] 　　　　　　　　　 O	S₁ (AuxV) V₁　[The N which S₂ V₂] 　　　　　　　　　 O

Underline the clause in each sentence.

1. Harrison Ford 以前演的電影我都很喜歡。

2. 上個月我看了兩次Amy Tan 寫的小說。

3. 我受不了他昨天做的飯，太難吃了。

4. 你最喜歡聽誰唱的歌？

 IV. Listening

1. Which movie has B seen?
   a. *Joy Luck Club.*
   b. *Wedding Banquet.*
   c. *Kitchen God's Wife.*
   d. *Eat, Drink, Men, Women.*

2. In B's opinion, how is that novel?
   a. Very boring.
   b. Very exciting.
   c. Very interesting.
   d. Very sad.

3. What does B think about the performance of the actor and the actress?
   a. The actor's performance was excellent, but the actress performed poorly.
   b. The actress's performance was excellent, but the actor performed poorly.
   c. Both the actor and the actress performed excellently.
   d. Both the actor and the actress performed poorly.

4. What is women's status in China now?
   a. Women's status in the society is still lower than that of men.
   b. Women's status in the society is higher than that of men.
   c. Women have equal status with men.

V. Speaking

A. Talk about yourself
Use the following questions as cues.

1. 你喜歡看電影嗎？看什麼樣的電影？

2. 你最近看了什麼電影？那個電影好看嗎？為什麼？

3. 你最喜歡哪個演員？為什麼？他/她演的片子你看過幾部？

4. 你看過中國電影嗎？你覺得中國電影怎麼樣？

B. Movie of the Year
Talk to your classmates to find out what movies they have seen this year and which one they like the best.

	Movies	Excellent	Good	Fair	Poor
1.					
2.					
3.					
4.					
5.					
6.					
7.					
8.					
9.					
10.					

C. Go to the library to check out a Chinese movie video and watch it with your classmates. After watching the film, discuss the following questions.

　　1. What do you think about the movie in general?
　　2. Do you like it or not? Why?
　　3. What do you think about the performance of the leading actor/actress and the supporting actor/actress (男配角 nánpèijiǎo/女配角 nǔpèijiǎo)
　　4. Do you like acting? Why/Why not?

D. Suppose that you and your friend both have seen *Star Trek* (or some other American movie). Discuss the same questions in C with your friend. You may use the title of the movie and name of the actor/actress in English, but use other structures and vocabulary in Chinese.

E. Talk about what kind of movie you like. You may need to use the following vocabulary.

科幻片	kēhuànpiàn	science fiction film
愛情片	àiqíngpiàn	love story film
偵探片	zhēntànpiàn	detective film
恐怖片	kǒngbùpiàn	horror film
武打片	wǔdǎpiàn	Chinese gongfu film

F. Talk about what kind of TV program you like to watch. You may need to use the following vocabulary.

脫口秀	tuōkǒuxiù	talk show
連續劇	liánxùjù	soap opera
新聞節目	xīnwén jiémù	news program
體育節目	tǐyù jiémù	sports program
綜藝節目	zòngyì jiémù	miscellaneous program
猜獎節目	cāijiǎng jiémù	price guessing program
教育節目	jiàoyù jiémù	education program
兒童節目	értóng jiémù	children's program

VI. Reading

A. Check your comprehension of the lesson dialogue by deciding whether the statements are true or false.

T / F   1.   Lǐ Míng yí .ge lǐbài méi chīfàn, suǒ.yǐ hěn è.

李明一個禮拜沒吃飯，所以很餓。

T / F   2.   Lǐ Míng jué.de sùshè .de fàn ràng rén dǎo wèikǒu.

李明覺得宿舍的飯讓人倒胃口。

T / F   3.   Lín Měiyīng kànwán .le diànyǐng, jué.de hěn nánguò.

林美英看完了電影，覺得很難過。

T / F   4.   Lǐ Míng jué.de Zhōng.guó diànyǐng bù hǎo, yīn.wèi kànwán .le ràng rén xīn .lǐ bù shū.fú.

李明覺得中國電影不好，因爲看完了讓人心裏不舒服。

T / F   5.   Lín Měiyīng jué.de Xǐfúhuì zhè .ge piàn.zi tán .de shì mǔqīn hé nǚr .de guān.xī.

林美英覺得「喜福會」這個片子談的是母親和女兒的關係。

T / F   6.   Gāo Dézhōng jué.de Xǐfúhuì tán.dào nǚrén zài shèhuì shàng .de dìwèi.

高德中覺得「喜福會」談到女人在社會上的地位。

T / F   7.   Gāo Dézhōng hé Lǐ Míng kàn .le bù shǎo fùnǚ yánjiū .de shū.

高德中和李明看了不少婦女研究的書。

T / F   8.   Lǐ Míng xǐ.huān Xǐfúhuì zhè bù diànyǐng, yīn.wèi yǎnyuán dōu hěn piào.liàng.

李明喜歡「喜福會」這部電影，因爲演員都很漂亮。

T / F   9.   Lín Měiyīng jué.de Lǐ Míng .de kànfǎ hěn yǒuyì.si, tā hěn xiǎng tīng.

林美英覺得李明的看法 'view' 很有意思，她很想聽。

B. Read the Authentic Material
  1. Look at the show time tables and circle the cinema names that you can recognize.

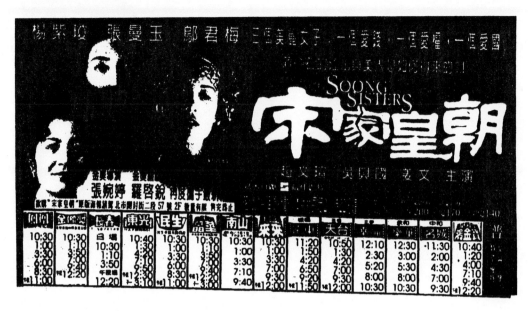

VII. Writing

A. Translate the following sentences into Chinese using topic-comment structure.

  1. As for the Japanese movie, he has never seen (it) once.

  2. As for songs, she sings very well; as for plays, she doesn't act well at all.

  3. I can speak Chinese well but cannot write even a single character.

  4. I have read all the novels that he wrote.

B. Translate the following into English and reorder them into a coherent passage.

  1. 以後他要去看中國電影，都要請小李一塊兒去。

  _____

  2. 他每個星期去看兩次。

  _____

3.　他說中國電影有意思倒是有意思，可是有的電影他看了很多次還不明白。

_____

4.　小高很喜歡看中國電影。

_____

5.　因為小李很懂中國電影。

_____

6.　The correct order for a coherent passage is: _____

C.　A Dog's Life

Write a short passage from the perspective of a dog or any animal/pet of your choice. Use the following patterns: (1) 不是 A, 就是 B, (2) S　每...VO # 次, (3) O, S　V過 # 次, (4) S　VO V得..., (5) S 要是... S 就...

第十二課 這件大衣怎麼樣？

I. Vocabulary

A. Look at the following picture and fill in the appropriate new words in pinyin.

chènshān

B. Write the pinyin and meaning for the following words and think of other words that can be modified by them.

1.	緊	jǐn	tight	靴子、褲子、衣服、大衣、外套
2.	冷	_____	_____	_____
3.	難過	_____	_____	_____
4.	自然	_____	_____	_____
5.	合適	_____	_____	_____

C. Choose the appropriate word(s) to complete the following sentences.

1. Nà jiā bǎihuò gōngsī zài dà (duìzhé, pāimài, dǎzhé), zán.men qù kàn.kàn .ba.

   那家百貨公司在大（對折、拍賣、打折），咱們去看看吧。

2. Zhè (tào, jiàn, tiáo) yīfú hěn hǎokàn, jiàqián yě bú guì.

   這（套、件、條）衣服很好看，價錢也不貴。

3. Zhè bù diànyǐng hěn yǒuyì.si, dàjiā (kěndìng, yóuqí, duōbànr) dōu huì xǐ.huān .de.

   這部電影很有意思，大家（肯定、尤其、多半兒）都會喜歡的。

4. Wǒ bù dǒng Zhōngwén, qǐng nǐ (jiào, bāng, ràng) wǒ xiě yí .ge hànzì.

   我不懂中文，請你（叫、幫、讓）我寫一個漢字。

5. Zhè .ge rén (kě bú.shì .ma, zhēn shì.de, hǎojí.le), nǐ yuè shuō tā yuè bù tīng.

   這個人（可不是嗎、眞是的、好極了），你越說他越不聽。

II. Characters

Hàn zì	長	短	貴	冷	且	穿	毛	衣	球	麵
Notes	cháng long 8	duǎn short 12	guì expensive 12	lěng cold 7	qiě moreover 5	chuān to wear 9	máo hair, fur 4	yī clothing 6	qiú ball, globe 11	miàn flour 20
1										
2										
3										
4										
5										
6										

	Compound/Phrase/Sentence/Memory Aid
長	
短	
貴	
冷	
且	
穿	
毛	
衣	
球	
麵	

Hàn zì	塊	錢	裏	頭	除	外	還	聽	寫	號
Notes	kuài M 13	qián money 16	lǐ inside 13	tóu head 16	chú except 10	wài outside 5	hái still 17	tīng listen 22	xiě write 15	hào number 13
1										
2										
3										
4										
5										
6										

Compound/Phrase/Sentence/Memory Aid

塊	
錢	
裏	
頭	
除	
外	
還	
聽	
寫	
號	

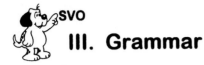

III. Grammar

A Major Sentence Patterns

1. 除了 ... (以外) construction

S 除了 N/VP (以外), 還/也 VO 除了 N/VP (以外), S 還/也 VO	Besides N/Ving O, S also VO
除了 A (以外), B 也 VO	Besides A, B also VO

1. 這個學期除了中文以外，你還選了什麼課？

   _____

2. 每天除了寫漢字以外，你也做什麼？

   _____

3. 這兒除了你以外，誰也會說一點兒中文？

   _____

2. 越 ... 越 ... construction

S (O) 越 V越 Adj	The more S V (O), the more Adj he/she becomes
S 越來越 Adj	S becomes more/much Adj-er
S_1 越 V(O), S_2 越 Adj	The more S_1 V (O), the more S_2 becomes Adj

1. 你中文怎麼樣？(the more I speak Chinese, the better it is.)

   _____

2. 這雙靴子怎麼樣？(the more I wear it, the more comfortable it is.)

   _____

3. 你覺得最近的天氣怎麼樣？

   _____

4. 老師說了以後，他懂不懂？

   _____

Ⓑ Usage of Common Phrases

1. V 來 V 去 expression

S （在 Place） V 來 V 去	S keeps on Ving back and forth (at a place)

1. Picasso 的畫兒(huàr 'painting')，你懂不懂？

   _____

2. 這家舊書店有沒有你要的書？(after searching for a while…)

   _____

3. 你覺得什麼飯最好吃？

   _____

2. Other usages of 的

X 的 N　→ X 的 V (O) 的 N → V (O) 的	X one the one that V(O)

Figure out the parts smeared by the whiteout in sentences 1-3.

1. 這家店裏，有的_____打對折，有的_____打八折。

2. 昨天看電影的_____很多。

3. 他寫的_____都不錯。

4. 這頂帽子怎麼樣？(The price is good.)

   $9.99 _____

5. 那雙手套怎麼樣？(They fit well.)

   _____

3. 打幾折 expression

打幾折？	How much is the discount?
打九折	(charge 90%) take 10% off
打八折	(charge 80%) take 20% off
打五/對折	(charge 50%) take 50% off
打四折	(charge 40%) take 60% off

1. 那件男毛衣打幾折？

_____

2. 那些褲子打八折嗎？

_____

3. 外套打幾折？

_____

4. Antonym compounds

大小	dàxiǎo	size	寬窄	kuānzhǎi	width
長短	chángduǎn	length	冷熱	lěngrè	temperature

1. How is the size of this coat (size 10)?

_____

2. How is the length of those pants?

_____

5. 號 as "size"

特大／大／中／小 號	extra-large/large/medium/small size
no. 號	size no.

1. 你穿幾號的襯衫？

_____

2. 你穿幾號的靴子？

_____

6. 有什麼好 V 的

X 有什麼好 V 的	What's the point of Ving X!

Choose an appropriate paraphrasing of the following.

_____1. 電視有什麼好看的！　a. 你不可以看電視。b. 看電視沒有意思。c. 看太多電視對人不好。

_____2. 煙有什麼好抽的！ a.抽煙對身體不好。 b. 這兒不能抽煙。 c.別抽煙了。

☾ Reentry

1. More on comparative construction

A　比 B Adj 嗎？	Is A Adj-er than B?
A　比 B Adj (得)多了/一點兒	A is (much more/a little bit) Adj-er than B
A 不比 B Adj	A is not as Adj as B
(A 跟 B), 哪 M (比較) Adj?	(As for A and B), which one is Adj-er?
A (比較) Adj	A is Adj-er
A　　　Adj(得)多了/一點兒	A is much more/ a little bit more Adj
A 有沒有 B (這麼 / 那麼) Adj ?	Is A as Adj as B?
A　(沒)有 B (這麼 / 那麼) Adj	A is (not) as Adj as B
A　跟 B　　一樣 Adj 嗎？	Are A and B equally Adj ?
A　跟 B(不) 一樣 Adj	A and B are (not) equally Adj
A 不跟 B　　一樣 Adj	A is not equally Adj with B

You are planning for a vacation during the winter break. Before you call the travel agent to book the ticket, you write down four questions for your friends who have been to both Florida and Arizona.

1. _____

2. _____

3. _____

4. _____

IV. Listening

1. Where does A suggest that B go?
   a. A grocery store.   c. A mall.
   b. A post office.   d. A bookstore.

2. Why is it that B doesn't want to go with A?
   a. Because things sold there are not very good.   c. Because B doesn't have money.
   b. Because things sold there are very expensive.   d. Because B doesn't need anything.

3. The dialogue suggests that the current season is:
   a. Winter.   c. Summer.
   b. Spring.   d. Fall.

4. What does B suggest that A buy?
    a. A pair of skorts.   c. A skirt.
    b. A pair of shorts.   d. A dress.

V. Speaking

A. Talk about yourself
    Use the following questions as cues.
    1. 你喜歡看籃球嗎？你自己打不打籃球？你籃球打得怎麼樣？

    2. 你都去哪兒買東西？你為什麼喜歡去那兒買東西？那兒的東西有折扣嗎？

    3. 父親節(Fùqīnjié 'Father's Day)你買什麼給你爸爸呢？為什麼買那個東西？母親節呢？

    4. 今年冬天流行穿什麼樣的衣服？你自己喜歡穿什麼樣的衣服？

B. Fashion Talk
    Explain to a new student who just came to this country the styles in 1970 (qīshí niándài), '80, and '90, answering questions such as:

    1. Do women like to wear long skirts or short skirts, high heeled or low heeled shoes?
    2. Do men wear formal dress such as suits and ties most of the time?
    3. Do children wear tight jeans or extra large pants?

C. Chat with your friend about the weather in your hometown. Compare it to the weather of the place you are living now. Include the pattern S 越來越 …. and S (O) 越 V 越 Adj.

D. Role Play
    Take the part of the customer or the salesperson. The customer has $70.00 and wants to purchase two clothing items. S/he wears size 8 sweater/shirt and size 10 overcoat. S/he checks and compares the price and size of various items with the help of the salesperson, who is looking at the store catalogue.

	紅	白	黑	藍
毛衣	$25.00	$20.00	$30.00	$25.00
Size	8-9	10-12	8-10	10-12
外套	$45.00	$45.00	$45.00	$45.00
Size	8-9	10-12	8-12	8-10
襯衫	$30.00	$30.00	$30.00	$30.00
Size	8-9	8-12	10-12	8-12

VI. Reading

A. Read the Text

　Check your comprehension of the lesson dialogue by answering the following questions.

1. Xiǎo Lín jiào Xiǎo Wáng bié zuò shén.me?
　 Tā jiào Xiǎo Wáng gēn tā yíkuàir qù nǎr?

　小林叫小王別做什麼？她叫小王跟她一塊兒去哪兒？

2. Wáng Huá xǐ.huān qù shāngchǎng guàng .ma? Wèishén.me?

　王華喜歡去商場逛嗎？爲什麼？

3. Wèishén.me Lín Měiyīng xiǎng qù shāngchǎng kàn.kàn?

　爲什麼林美英想去商場看看？

4. Wáng Huá wèishén.me juédìng qù shāngchǎng .le? Tā xiǎng mǎi shén.me dōng.xi?

　王華爲什麼決定去商場了？她想買什麼東西？

5. Wáng Huá jué.de nèi jiàn lánsè .de dàyī zěn.meyàng?

　王華覺得那件藍色的大衣怎麼樣？

6. Wáng Huá shuō nèi jiàn kāfēisè .de dàyī zěn.meyàng?

　王華說那件咖啡色的大衣怎麼樣？

7. Lín Měiyīng jué.de Wáng Huá yīnggāi mǎi shén.meyàng .de dàyī? Wèishén.me?

　林美英覺得王華應該買什麼樣的大衣？爲什麼？

8. Wèishén.me Lín Měiyīng yào Wáng Huá zài mǎi jiàn hēisè .de qúnkù?

　爲什麼林美英要王華再買件黑色的裙褲？

9. Lín Měiyīng mǎi .le shén.me dōng.xi?

　林美英買了什麼東西？

B. Read the Authentic Material

1. Read the advertisement on the right and indicate whether the statements are true or false.

____ a. This report forecasts today's weather in Taiwan.

____ b. If you plan to go out in Taipei, you have to bring an umbrella with you.

____ c. The lowest temperature in Taiwan is 25° C.

明日台灣天氣　註：氣溫偏攝氏

地區	天氣	高溫	低溫
台北市	晴午後多雲	35	26
基隆北海岸	晴時多雲	34	26
台北桃園	晴午後多雲	34	26
新竹苗栗	晴午後多雲	33	26
台中彰化	晴午後多雲	33	26
雲林嘉義	晴午後多雲	33	26
台南高雄	晴午後多雲	33	27
屏東	晴午後多雲	33	27
花蓮	多雲時晴	33	25
澎湖	晴時多雲	33	26

今日大陸天氣　註：氣溫為攝氏

城市	天氣	高溫	低溫
廣州	多雲	31	23
福州	晴天	30	23
昆明	多雲	22	14
重慶	雨天	24	17
漢口	雨天	25	16
杭州	多雲	22	17
上海	多雲	23	17
南京	多雲	23	15
青島	晴天	22	16
北京	晴天	22	10
開封	多雲	23	12
西安	多雲	20	10
瀋陽	晴天	20	9
蘭州	多雲	17	8
海口	多雲	31	24

2. Read the advertisement on the left and choose a correct answer.

____ a. This report forecasts (1) today's (2) tomorrow's (3) the day after tomorrow's weather in mainland China.

____ b. According to this report, (1) four (2) three (3) two cities will have rain.

____ c. The capital, Beijing, will be (1) cloudy (2) sunny (3) rainy.

____ d. (1) Guangzhou (2) Shanghai (3) Xi'an will have the highest temperature in China.

3. Read the following advertisement and choose a correct answer.

＿＿＿ a. The sale will last about (1) two days (2) three days (3) four days.

＿＿＿ b. The sale occurs in (1) April (2) March (3) February.

＿＿＿ c. The sales items are (1) dining set (2) carpets (3) Chinese crafts (4) all of the above.

印第安那州
印第安那玻里市

········· 全部貨品 ·········

公開大拍賣

數月來中國產品展及展銷會，感謝華人們的大力支持，二月份舉行此一存貨公開大拍賣，全部存貨函蓋萬餘呎展示間，包括各式紅木實用傢俬，中國古典傢俬，玉石巧雕，瓷部、景泰藍各式藝術品及大批中國天津地毯，生絲地毯，保證是您在同一地點所見最多選擇的中國傢俱、工藝、地毯大結合。

三日公開

拍賣時間：(三日五場大拍賣)
　　星期三：二月十九日　　下午7：00起
　　星期四：二月二十日　　下午1：00及7：00起
　　星期五：二月二十一日　下午1：00及7：00起

拍賣地點：**Whitley Shopping Center**
　　　　　1345 Pine Circle Drive

三日公開
敬請光臨

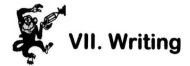

VII. Writing

A. To buy or not to buy

Answer the questions by providing a reason for your decision (comparing the size and price). Refer to the information provided in the chart.

	大小	價錢
白毛衣	10 號	$ 40.50
紅毛衣	8 號	$ 38.50
黑外套	9 號	$ 80.00
藍外套	11 號	$150.00
黑靴子	7 號半	$120.00

1. Do you want to buy the white sweater or the red one?

2. Do you want to buy the black overcoat or the blue one?

3. Do you want to buy the black overcoat or the black boots?

B. You will take a trip to China and plan to buy some gifts for your family. Jot down the preferred color and size of various clothing items, shoes, or accessories your family members wear and write a brief passage to remind yourself what you plan to buy. You may want to include the patterns: (1)除了 N/VO 以外，S 還/也..., (2)除了 A 以外, B 也...

我要買一件紅的毛衣給媽媽。

I. Vocabulary

A. Organize the following words into a net, tree, flow chart, or diagram. Display and explain it to your classmates.

huǒjī	火雞
fàngjià	放假
Gǎn'ēnjié	感恩節
dù.zi	肚子
yùndòngchǎng	運動場
chāojí shìchǎng	超級市場
dà chī dà hē	大吃大喝
kǒufú	口福

B. Make a sentence that incorporates a word suggested by the picture.

1. _____

2. _____

3. _____

4. _____

C. Identify appropriate responses to the phrases in the left column.

____ 1. 這個給你。   a. 對不起。

____ 2. 我來幫你。   b. 別開玩笑了。

____ 3. 你打錯電話了。   c. 怎麼好意思。

____ 4. 說真的，你快找個男朋友吧！   d. 可不是嗎？

____ 5. 我昨天沒去打工。   e. 你真是的。

____ 6. 那本書寫得真好。   f. 好極了。

II. Characters

Hàn zì	送	行	門	口	回	家	宿	舍	放	假
Notes	sòng to send 10	xíng be fine 6	mén door 8	kǒu mouth 2	huí to return 6	jiā family 10	sù lodge 11	shè a house 8	fàng to put 8	jià holiday 11
1										
2										
3										
4										
5										
6										

	Compound/Phrase/Sentence/Memory Aid
送	
行	
門	
口	
回	
家	
宿	
舍	
放	
假	

Hàn zì	星	期	玩	笑	火	雞	鐘	節	市	只
Notes	xīng star 9	qī period 12	wán to play 8	xiào laugh 10	huǒ fire 4	jī chicken 18	zhōng clock 20	jié holiday 15	shì market 5	zhǐ merely 5
1										
2										
3										
4										
5										
6										

	Compound/Phrase/Sentence/Memory Aid
星	
期	
玩	
笑	
火	
雞	
鐘	
節	
市	
只	

SVO

III. Grammar

Ⓐ Major Sentence Patterns

1. 坐 ...到/回 ...來/去 construction

S (要) 坐 Conveyance 到/回 Place 來/去 VO	S come/go to Place to VO by Conveyance

1. 你感恩節回家了嗎？你怎麼回去的？

_____

2. 你每天怎麼來學校上課？

_____

3. 你要怎麼到機場搭飛機？

_____

2. 是坐 ...到/回 ...來/去的 construction

S 是坐 Conveyance 到 Place 來/去的嗎？	Is it by Conveyance that S come/go to Place? Did S come/go to Place by Conveyance?

1. 你坐小巴到機場去嗎？

不，我是 _____

2. 你搭飛機到布城(Bùchéng 'Bloomington'; or other cities) 來嗎？

不，我_____

3. 你開車上圖書館去嗎？

不，我_____

4. _____

他想坐小巴從芝加哥到舊金山去。

5. _____

我們要開車從布城到紐約去。

3. 從 …坐 …到 …來 /去 construction

S (MTA) (要) 從 Place₁ 坐 Conveyance 到 Place₂ 來/去	(Time) S (will) come/ go
S (MTA) (要) 坐 Conveyance 從 Place₁ 到 Place₂ 來/去	from Place₁ to Place₂ by Conveyance

You want to take a trip to somewhere. Plan the trip considering the money ($300) you have, the time, and the transportation vehicle.

1. Mark where you are and where you want to go on the map.

2. Identify where you plan to stop on your way there.

3. Specify how you will go from one place to the next, e.g.,

我要從布城開車到芝加哥，從芝加哥搭飛機到⋯

_____

4. Pivotal construction

S₁ V₁ [O₁/S₂ V₂ O₂]	S₁ V₁O₁ to V₂O₂

1. 你爸媽請誰來你家過感恩節？

_____

2. 你爸媽常(cháng 'often')叫你別做什麼？

_____

5. 只要… 就… construction

S 只要 Adv VO 就…	So (As) long as S VO…/Only if S VO…then…
只要 S Adv VO 就…	
只要 VO　　　 S 就…	
只要 No M N　 就…	(It) takes only No M…

1. 我下星期一要交期末報告，怎麼辦？

_____

2. 我最近重了好幾磅，怎麼辦？

_____

3. 從你家開車到學校來要多久(duójiǔ, 'how long') ？

_____

ⓑ Usage of Common Phrases

1. 多/少 V一點兒 O expressions

多V一點兒 O	V a little bit more of O
少V一點兒 O	V a little bit less of O

Give me advice.

1. 我太重了，肚子也有一點兒大。

_____

2. 我累極了。

_____

3. 我中文說得不太好。

_____

2. ...的時候 expression

S [Adj/VO 的時候], ... (movable)	When S is/was/are/were Adj/Ving...,
NP 的時候, ...	At the time of NP, ...

1. 放假的時候，你每天都做什麼？

_____

2. 你請客的時候，應該做什麼？

_____

3. 你上課的時候，不可以做什麼？

_____

3. The suggestion and command particle 吧

S 快VO吧！	Let's (hurry and) go to VO!
(S)快V(O)！	(S) hurry and go to VO!

1. Let's hurry and catch the bus!

   _____

2. Go work out in the gym!

   _____

3. Write your paper quickly!

   _____

4. **Better not VO expression**

可別 VO 才好！	(X) better not VO!

Be my friend and give me candid comments.

1. 你吃這麼多糖，_____

2. 你喝這麼多咖啡，_____

3. 你天天看這麼多電視，_____

5. 再 vs. 又

S MTA 又 (要)　 VO (了)	S (will) VO again
S MTA 又　　　 VO (了)	S did VO again
S MTA 　　(要)再 VO	S will VO again

Fill in the blanks with 再 or 又

1. 小李去年回中國去，今年_____要回去。他說他得去看看他的父母，明年
   只要他有錢，他會_____回去。

2. 別_____說了！你昨天告訴我他不來，今天_____說他會來，你是在跟我開
   玩笑嗎？

6. **Subject omission**

S₁ VP₁, VP₂, VP₃...	S₁ VP₁, S₁ VP₂, S₁ VP₃...

Delete the unnecessary subjects from the following paragraph.

1. 我星期五一早就走了，我搭朋友的車到機場。我在那兒等了二十分鐘，
   飛機就來了。我上了飛機以後，我在機上先看了一點兒書，我再休息半
   個鐘頭就到了。

C Reentry

1. More on ...的N construction

| 到 Place 去/來 的 N | The N that goes/comes to Place |

1. 在布城什麼很方便？(taking a bus that comes to school)

_____

2. 這兒什麼人很多？(those who have been abroad)

_____

3. 在大學裏，什麼樣的學生很努力？(those who study Chinese)

_____

 ## IV. Listening

1. How did A go to his friend's house?
   a. By car.
   b. By bus.
   c. By airplane.
   d. On foot.

2. How long did it take to get to his friend's house?
   a. Over 30 minutes.
   b. Over 20 minutes.
   c. Over 40 minutes.
   d. Over 10 munites.

3. How does Xiao Li look now?
   a. He looks slimmer.
   b. He looks taller.
   c. He looks heavier.
   d. He looks much more handsome.

4. What did A suggest that Xiao Li do?
   a. A suggested that he exercise.
   b. A suggested that he go on a diet.
   c. A suggested that he eat more.
   d. A suggested running.

V. Speaking

A. Talk about yourself
Use the following questions as cues.
1. 你最喜歡過哪個節？為什麼？

2. 過節的時候，你吃什麼特別的東西？做什麼特別的事？

3. 你覺得美國人好客不好客？為什麼？

4. 你喜歡開玩笑嗎？你跟你的朋友開什麼樣的玩笑？

B. Talk about a holiday
Describe a holiday that you have in mind including the activities people usually do on that occasion. Then, have your classmates guess which holiday you are talking about.

	Holidays	*Name*	*Date*	*Activities*
1.				
2.				
3.				
4.				
5.				
6.				

C. Car pooling
You don't have a car but you need to go to the library every day (otherwise it will be a twenty-minute walk), do grocery shopping once a week, go to a movie or concert once a month, and go to the airport once in a while. Talk to your classmates to find out their means of transportation to various places and see if you can arrange a car-pooling plan with them.

VI. Reading

A. Read the Text

Check your comprehension of the lesson dialogue by answering the following questions.

1. Lín Měiyīng Gǎn'ēnjié .de shí.hòu huíjiā .le méi.yǒu? Tā shì zěn.me zǒu .de?

林美英感恩節的時候回家了沒有？她是怎麼走的？

2. Wèishén.me tā bù dā Gāo Dézhōng .de chē dào jīchǎng?

為什麼她不搭高德中的車到機場？

3. Lín Měiyīng jué.de sùshè hǎo hái.shì jiā.lǐ hǎo? Wèishén.me?

林美英覺得宿舍好還是家裏好？為什麼？

4. Gāo Dézhōng Gǎn'ēnjié .de shíhòu huíjiā .le .ma? Wèishén.me?

高德中感恩節的時候回家了嗎？為什麼？

5. Gāo Dézhōng chī .le huǒjī méi.yǒu? Shì tā zìjǐ zuò .de .ma?

高德中吃了火雞沒有？是他自己做的嗎？

6. Lǐ Míng Gǎn'ēnjié .de shí.hòu zuò .le shén.me?

李明感恩節的時候做了什麼？

7. Lǐ Míng Gǎn'ēnjié guò .le yǐhòu, děi zuò shén.me? Wèishén.me?

李明感恩節過了以後，得做什麼？為什麼？

8. Gāo Dézhōng gēn Lǐ Míng kāi .le shén.me wánxiào?

高德中跟李明開了什麼玩笑？

9. Wèishén.me Lín Měiyīng xiǎng qù yùndòngchǎng duàn.liàn?

為什麼林美英想去運動場鍛練？

B. Read the Authentic Material

1. Read the following and figure out the answers:

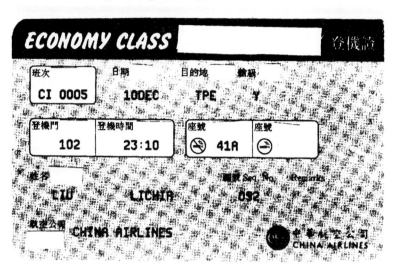

a. What is this ticket for?

_____

b. When is the traveling time?

_____

c. Which gate should the traveler take?

_____

d. What is the number of the seat?

_____

2. Read the following story and answer the questions.

a. What holiday did the author and her family observe?

_____

b. How did they observe the occasion?

_____
_____
_____
_____

c. What did the author's family and their friends do after dinner?

_____
_____
_____

感恩節

張美英

十一月二十七日是感恩節。那一天我爸爸媽媽請了幾個剛來美國的中國朋友到我們家來,一塊兒慶祝感恩節。媽媽烤了一隻大火雞,做了一些沙拉,麵包,紅薯,兩個南瓜派,和一個大蛋糕。我們四點鐘就開始吃飯。爸爸先帶領我們禱告,感謝上帝讓我們都健康快樂。吃完飯以後,我們一塊兒看了一場電視球賽。看完球賽,爸爸就送那幾個朋友回去了。每年的感恩節,我們都過得很愉快。

VII. Writing

A. Write a thank-you note to your host family who invited you over for Thanksgiving. Remember to thank them for their hospitality and indicate how you felt about the occasion celebrated.

B. You will go to China via Japan 日本 Rìběn next month. Write a letter to your Japanese friend. The letter should include:

1. An apology for not being able to write sooner, e.g., you are working on a term paper.

2. A detailed travel plan, e.g., you will fly from Chicago 芝加哥 Zhījiāgē to SanFrancisco 舊金山 Jiùjīnshān and take Amtrak to Seattle 西雅圖 Xīyǎtú for sightseeing along the West Coast.

3. Some requests, e.g., asking your friend to pick you up at the airport or help in collecting information about schedules, etc.